I AM
another
YOU

by priya kumar

I AM
another
YOU

by priya kumar

Edited by: Sonavi Desai

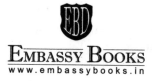

EMBASSY BOOKS

www.embassybooks.in

I AM another**YOU**

by priya kumar

© Priya Kumar
First Published in India: 2009

Published by:
EMBASSY BOOK DISTRIBUTORS
120, Great Western Building,
Maharashtra Chamber of Commerce Lane,
Fort, Mumbai-400 023, (India)
Tel : (+91-22) 22819546 / 32967415
email : embassy@vsnl.com
Website: www.embassybooks.in

ISBN 10: 93-80227-17-5
ISBN 13: 978-93-80227-17-7

Book and Cover Design: Namrata Chattaraj.
e-mail: namzie@gmail.com

Printed and Bound in India by
M/s. Decora Book Prints Pvt. Ltd.

Acknowledgements

· ·

We are made up of a thousand others.
We are shaped by people, their opinions,
their thoughts, their presence and their energy

I owe this book to so many people who directly and indirectly supported and influenced me in my journey of making this possible.

I thank my grandparents, Ramrakha and Prakash for bringing me up the way they did; my parents Kirti and Sona for making me the person I am; my brother Kapil for his unwavering support; my sister-in-law Suchita for her encouragement always; Aarya, my niece and god-daughter, for her divine presence; my dogs : Betty, who now lives in dog heaven, and Coco, who I can't have enough of, for their unconditional love and devotion; and my housekeepers, Tarsi and Suvarna, for making my life so easy and organised.

I thank my friend, Nigam, for his unending belief and support in all that I do; Bunty and Rajnish, for always succeeding to lift my spirits; Shashi, Deepak, Komal and Disha, for being my extended family and Raghu, for supporting me through all my decisions.

I thank my publisher, Sohin Lakhani for believing in me without even seeing my work and allowing me the pace and space to express myself. My special thanks to my team: Aarti, Leslie, Priyanka and Ashish, who really supported me with their love and commitment during the entire time that

I wrote the book. I owe special thanks to Aarti for making my connection with my publisher; without her help this book would not have seen the light of day. I thank Amrita for her commitment and support over the years that she worked with me. I thank Vishal for discovering the writer in me and creating magic with my work. I thank Sonavi Desai for the speedy and beautiful editing.

I acknowledge my teachers and mentors, Dr. Niranjan Patel, Kurt Rinck, Peggy Dylan and William Horton for teaching me life lessons through experience and by example.

I thank all my relatives for their love, encouragement and prayers.

I express my gratitude to all those who I met in my journey of growth for having taught me and propelled me to grow through experiences that were sometimes joyous and sometimes painful. I am grateful for them all.

Contents

Introduction

• •

I went to the Netherlands in April 2004. It was a tough journey to take, simply because it was an escape; an escape into the unknown.

I spent close to a month living with the natives of Netherlands along with fourth generation shamans. The shamans are an ancient tribe who indulge in spiritual processes for their evolution and freedom. I took the opportunity to take part in their processes; it blew my mind and set my spirit free. It was similar to the process of tearing down an old building to construct a new one. When I reached the Netherlands I was an old run down building infested with junk. And when I took the plane back, I was the new villa on the block; neighbour's envy, owner's pride.

Ever since that trip, the unknown has always fascinated me. The element of surprise and discovery is contained in the unknown. Life sometimes becomes too familiar and too predictable. Today seems like yesterday and tomorrow holds the certainty of the past. What a boring existence that would be!

The unknown brings adventure, it brings growth, it brings with it the promise of change and progress, it brings a new beginning and an end to the old. I have embraced every opportunity ever since to take that step towards the thrill of not knowing what will happen next. A step forward into the unknown has more power than a stationary existence.

In the pages to follow I have spanned my journey through a few processes that contributed towards the transformation into who I am today. I have shared with you my most intimate realisations and my most valued lessons. Every time I attempted to share my experiences and my growth as a result of these processes with friends or others in my seminars, I found that they too were seeking the same answers, and they rejoiced and grew in the narration of my story. I found that we are all on the same path, that we all seek the same things and that we all feel the same way; the degrees may vary but the basic intent stays. I realised that there is no you separate from me.

Writing this book was a great experience for me. It gave me an opportunity to look at my journey through the spirit of my teachers. It gave me an opportunity to feel compassion for my old personality and celebrate the one that I have become. It gave me a chance to understand better what my teachers did not say, or what they said that I did not then understand. It allowed me the grace to appreciate who I have become as a result of those processes and how my life has changed towards progress and success ever since. And in all humility, in writing this book I became aware about how many lives I have indirectly touched and influenced because I became a better me.

I hope that you will have as much fun reading the book as I had writing it. Putting pen to paper and baring my soul was one of my greatest achievements. I hope that somewhere at some point you will realise that You are another Me and that we will be able to establish the bond that we all are afraid to make. I have made an attempt to reach out to you and I am making you the beneficiary of my struggles and subsequent victory.

I invite you to take this journey with me, a journey that will lead you to your own personal breakthrough and to your life's purpose.

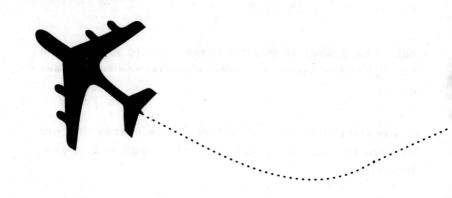

The End

- -

Everything had ended. My world had collapsed before my eyes and I didn't know how it had all happened.

"One coffee, please," I said to the coffee vendor at the boarding gate lounge.

"Which flavour would you like?" he asked politely.

"It doesn't matter." I was not interested in the coffee; I was not interested in life.

I was on my way to boarding the plane to Amsterdam. Up north, ahead of a little town called Winterswijk, I was to meet a family that would take me to the rituals of "Spiritual Freedom" by an ancient shaman tribe.

"Are you mad?" my mother had yelled. She had said the same thing when I decided to quit my MBA and continue with my profession as a tuition teacher. That's the exact tone she had used when I used up all my savings to start my career as a motivational speaker. And those were the same words she had used as a threat when I told her I wanted to break my relationship with my long standing boyfriend.

"Miss! Your coffee!" The vendor sounded alarmed. I had been standing there for quite a few minutes looking blank and his customers were queuing up behind me. Startled, I took the coffee and I could feel the silent "tsk tsk" of the people behind me. "Kids today . . ." I heard one lady telling another, the familiar tale of how our generation was going to the dogs.

I had heard so much about the shamans and their rituals had always intrigued me. This was my opportunity to find out what it was all about. My business had fallen apart and I needed to escape. I wanted to turn back the clock, not to just four years ago when I was the queen of business and love, but to centuries ago where existed a higher intelligence whose predictions we are living by today.

"Shamans are cannibals," my friends told me, aghast at my decision to undergo tribal processes in an alien land. They believed that their familiar life of misery was better than a potentially beautiful unknown one. So they went on, painstakingly weaving their known past into a known future that promised only more misery.

People I trusted with my life had eaten away at my existence and cheated me of all that I owned so cannibals did not frighten me. I guess a person who is defeated does not know fear any more. He is already prepared to go further down. He is even prepared to die. You can't scare or threaten a person who has lost all hope in life.

"Amsterdam is the city of drugs and sex. You will be ruined. Didn't you hear that case about blah blah blah?" I don't even remember who said this because they all said similar things. Nothing mattered. I was going to stay with the shamans where I thought it would be safe to live in freedom.

The shamans are ancient tribesmen still residing in the north of Europe and south of America. They indulge in rituals which are said to set your spirit free and ignite you to your purpose. I had taken all the money that I had, and it wasn't much. I was fully prepared to live the rest of my life in the tribal ways of the shamans if I had to; after all I had nothing to come back to.

When you lose, people start treating you as though you are naive and foolish. Suddenly even your retarded next door neighbour whose sole purpose in life was women, parties and drugs becomes an intelligent adviser. "You know what? You should find a rich man and settle down. With your intelligence and good looks it will be a piece of cake. I'm going to a party tonight and I know some people, why don't you come along?" was his condolatory advice to me.

"I hope I have packed enough . . ." My thoughts were dancing like a restless monkey. "I hope Fleur, comes to pick me up at the airport because I have no idea how to get to Winterswijk or to the village from there." Fleur, who was a friend's friend in Amsterdam, had sounded very uncertain when she had said, "I will surely be there."

"You must learn to compromise," my father had counselled. "That is the way of life after all. Men are made this way, they cheat, and they falter. It is a woman's duty to forgive and move on." I didn't want any more sermons on compromise. I can forgive but I can't compromise on what my heart knows is right. How do you compromise on the fact that the man you loved so deeply loved you . . . and someone else too?

"Priya!" I heard a voice call and almost spilt my coffee, untouched and cold. I turned around and saw a stranger walking towards me. "I attended your workshop last week. You are amazing." He was beaming and so excited to see me. "I actually didn't want to attend the session and had planned to walk out in the tea break but you had me hooked . . ." But I was no longer listening to him. The thought of never coming back to India overtook me. I was leaving my familiar world with no intention of returning and this stranger's words or presence did not matter to me.

"You are going to Amsterdam for a workshop?" He had to ask twice before I replied. "Yes," I said, totally lost.

"This is the last and final call for Miss P. Kumar," the public announcement system blared.

"Oh that's you! You better run!" the man said. I had even forgotten to ask his name.

I handed him my untouched coffee and darted towards the boarding gate.

I was the last to enter the aircraft. I sat in my seat and said my final goodbye to the world I knew so well. It was the end.

I sat at the garden table sipping hot coffee. It was beautiful. Open fields around, a beautiful cottage, chilly weather, dogs running in the background, flowers waiting to bloom, clear skies; I loved it. The scene was straight out of the pictures I had torn out of a travel magazine and stuck on my vision board. I believed that if I could put pictures of my dreams on a board which I could see every day, they would certainly come true. As magical as it may sound, my vision board has mapped the journey of my life. I have been led to every dream, every desire that I had carefully cut and pasted on my vision board. And now, being here seemed a conspiracy of my own desire.

Mary was the housekeeper of the B&B I stayed at. She was plump and seemed in her late forties. She looked like my grandmother, only a younger and modern version. The place was nothing fancy, just a small cottage. People visiting the town would often stay there. There was a kitchen, dining area, one bedroom with four bunk beds, one toilet and bath and a garden area with a nice table. That was it. You couldn't ask for more for eight euros a night.

Fleur had not come to pick me up. I had expected it all along. By now I am good at picking up on deceit. I had just had a close encounter with the biggest con job of my life. My business partner had fled with my share of the business and the money. My seven years of hard work was cashed in by this charming person who, under the pretext of expanding my business, had shrunk my empire to zero. Now I was a pro at recognising lies a mile away. I had to struggle with two heavy suitcases and find myself a train ticket to Winterswijk. "You can't take these bags," the taxi driver said. He had the smallest car in the world and that was the only taxi around. The town was thirty kilometres up north. I threw in a few clothes and essentials in a rucksack the taxi driver lent me, leaving my two gigantic suitcases in security at the train station for five euros a day. So much for carrying "all I needed"!

It was an interesting start to the journey of spiritual freedom. I guess when you have lost all hope, even defeat cannot defeat you. You can't kill someone twice.

When I had walked into the cottage with my rucksack Mary had looked at me quizzically and said, "Boy, you travel light. Come, you must be jetlagged. Let me make you some breakfast and then you can get some rest." Taking my rucksack she had led me into the dainty little cottage.

As I sipped my coffee and nibbled on some plain bread, Mary came out smiling. "Kahuna is our spiritual leader here. I have told him about you. I don't want to push you because you have just arrived but he suggested we start the rituals tomorrow. It seems to be an auspicious time to finish the rituals in the coming week. I recommend you rest all day today so you are just about ready to take part in one of the most potent processes towards spiritual cleansing and freedom." I nodded, not sure what lay ahead.

"Tomorrow is too early to start," I grumbled to myself.

All my life I had debated whether it was too early or too late for things I wanted to do and experience. It had never occurred to me that I had spent a great deal of my life in anticipation of the right time. The right time was always in the future, it was never now. I never understood that the only right time is always right now. Left to myself I would rather have engaged in the rituals a week later after having calmed the whining in my heart under the pretext of my jet lag. I wanted to be alone for a few days. I needed space to sulk in solitude. But Mary was on a mission to get me to commence the rituals in the auspicious week, and my fatigue and distress did not seem to bother her.

"I will introduce you to your roommates tonight. They will arrive this evening," she said, showing me around and giving me instructions about what was where in case I needed anything. "You are going to need a warm jacket," she said looking at me. I was wearing blue jeans and a plain white cotton t-shirt, shivering with every gush of breeze.

Mary darted in and came out with an oversized fur jacket. "Here, this will keep you warm."

I was grateful for the kindness. I was grateful for where I was. And above all I was grateful that I had some courage; that I could find the strength to break away from a painful past in search of a better future.

I guess even when you are defeated the flame of hope never dies out. I was here now. I wasn't defeated. Not yet.

I was tired. My body was exhausted, my soul torn. I needed to sleep.

I went up to the room and chose the bottom bunk. I had no energy to climb up. I slipped under the warm blankets and in a few seconds I was in deep sleep . . . blank . . . nothing.

"Dinner is ready." The loud voice made me jump out of my skin. "Where am I?" was the first thought. Jet lag and emotional pain were messing with my brain.

I looked around and saw three people in the room. "I'm Emma," the pretty lady said. Emma seemed in her early thirties, blue eyes, blond hair, thin frame. "This is Rick and this is Sain." The two heavy built men smiled but did not shake hands. Rick was lean and smiled with a dimple. Sain looked the oldest yet the fittest. They were sitting on the bed parallel to mine, unpacking. "We will be joining you in Kahuna's rituals. He is our spiritual master." Emma spoke with great respect about her master, Kahuna.

"Dinner is ready!" Mary shouted out again. I promptly hopped out of bed and headed down with the others.

At dinner we exchanged pleasantries, where we were from, what we did, how excited we were. It seemed like an altruistic world. My life before I took the flight began to fade away into the distance and I was happy.

After dinner we headed for the room. "You will need a good night's sleep," Mary had said, suggesting that we sleep early.

I slipped into bed. Just before I could close my eyes, I saw Rick and Sain undress to their skin. They hopped into bed, their own respective beds, naked. Emma was the next to strip and get into the bed parallel to mine. "You are going to sleep with your clothes on?" she queried.

"Err, umm, yeah," I answered.

"That's weird," she muttered and drifted off to sleep.

My experiences 'lessoned' for you:

···> Life does not always go your way and sometimes things will go wrong. That is the excitement of being alive. The only place where there are no problems is the graveyard.

···> You cannot solve problems from the same place that you created them. You need neutral ground to find a solution.

···> It is ok to take a break when you are hurting. Make sure the break is not in the same environment as the hurt. Even taking a walk in the park is a break as long as it is not the same place where your troubles started.

···> Sometimes the company of wise people encourages you to seek solutions to your problem.

···> If you are alive there is hope and where there is hope, life and happiness will follow.

The Sweat Lodge

I woke up in the morning in a daze with the alarm beeping its lungs off. I was beginning to feel uncomfortable. Sleeping with half-naked strangers was not my idea of a pretty morning. I'm a very effusive person. Even though I hate waking up early, my "good morning" is the chirpiest greeting of the day. Sleepy eyes, croaky voice, messy hair but definitely high voltage energy. My good morning even via a text message to friends reflects my excitement to wake up to the world. But here it was different. My "good morning" was more subdued, with minimal eye contact. I was carefully avoiding conversation with my roommates who I dreaded would tell me to sleep without my clothes on!

Shower time was agony. I have fiercely guarded my privacy all my life and to shower in a cubicle with a broken lock put me through a real mental challenge. I left the water running from the minute I entered the shower to the time I got out to let my presence be "heard". I realised that my roommates were so "native" that none of them had travelled out of their country or even taken a flight to understand an "Occupied" or "Do not disturb" sign. So after having Emma barge into the loo the previous night when I was taking a leak I decided that wasting some water to preserve my sanity was worth it.

Rick popped his head into the cubicle. "Let's go, lady! The water won't cleanse your spirit . . . or your body!" he said, deliberately eyeing me to make me uncomfortable.

I was the last to leave the room. I knew making my bed would set me back by another minute and I decided to break the rule of "making the bed before you leave" and run to the farm.

It was a chilly morning but the clear sky with scattered, spotless white clouds made up for the shivers that ran down my spine. I could literally feel my soul grow just connecting with the ever expansive blue of the sky. The pine trees were wet and green, whether from the dew or the drizzle didn't really matter; I was curious and excited about meeting Kahuna, the great spiritual master, a fourth generation shaman.

There he was, sitting on the garden chair. Long hair, rustic look, unshaven, taller than any man I had ever seen; a man with the wisest countenance and the most stunning smile. This was Kahuna, a gorgeous, timeless, spiritual master.

Emma, Rick, Sain and Mary were sitting at the table in animated conversation with Kahuna. The moment he saw me Kahuna left the conversation and walked towards me. With a smile he embraced me in a warm, tight hug. It was a huge bear hug and I was lost in his large frame. My head dug into his chest as he embraced my slight form. "Welcome to the world of spiritual freedom," he said, planting a kiss on my forehead.

Kahuna treated me as though he knew me, as though we had been together for a long time and I was returning home after a lengthy journey. I was expecting some sort of sermon or words of wisdom. There was none. There was laughter and there was joy. I was confused. Sometimes I think I am very foolish, I actually question happiness and clarity.

Emma abruptly started a chant and the others joined in. It was in a language that I didn't understand. Their dedicated chanting made me feel like a foreigner to the world of spirituality. But then I guess spirituality is more of a journey than a discipline at least that was what I told myself then.

"Today is an auspicious day. In fact, this whole week is a spiritually charged week. We will start the day with the Sweat Lodge ritual," Kahuna smiled.

"Let's go then, the sun will be up soon!" Emma stood up and started to lead the way. We all got up and walked along, my short steps failing to keep pace with their giant strides. Rick turned around and with an apologetic look I hastened my steps.

I had looked up references of the sweat lodge before I came to the farm. I like to know all I can on my own and then build on it as I experience that "knowing". I like to be prepared. I was looking forward to being a part of the ceremony and I was more proud than glad that I was here in the experience.

In one form or another, the sweat bath pervaded cultures from the Alaskan Eskimo to the Mayan. The purpose in most cases went beyond getting the body clean. The sweat bath provided a cure for illness, revitalisation for aching muscles, and a sense of racial identity. In many cultures the sweat lodge awakened you to your life's purpose. That was what I had come to seek.

A hundred yards away at a sudden clearing Kahuna was waiting for us with four other men. Their hair was long like Kahuna's, tied in a pony tail. They were dressed in thick earth coloured robes with brightly edged sleeves. "We have to find a location for the sweat lodge," Kahuna said. He had now pulled on a white robe of thick wool and carried a cat bone wand in his hand. As he pointed towards the sun he looked like the master I was hoping to find when I first saw him.

On getting our attention he turned around and started

to walk purposefully in the direction he had pointed out. Medicine men, ancient shamans and spiritual masters do not believe in making meaningless conversation.

As we walked out of the farm territory across the fields I felt my shoulders ache with the weight of my winter coat. I looked like a little girl trapped in a bear's body. I quietly followed in search of a spiritual place for the ceremony. I had no idea what a spiritual place was but went in search of it anyway. So many times in my life I have sought that perfect relationship with no idea what exactly it was! I felt as lost in my search now as I had all my life. But unlike earlier, what I had today was a team of spiritual masters leading the way.

In a while we came to a clearing. I don't know how far we had walked for my mind had been immersed in the past. I had journeyed much further mentally than physically and it had left me with the feeling of disorientation that I had lived with for most of my life. A few feet away I could see a pond, little bushes of wild flowers and a crow's nest in one of the tall trees nearby. The sky was clear and the trees swayed gently in the breeze. I inhaled the heady scent of the wild flowers and my senses came alive. From where I stood the field spread into infinity and I could almost see the curve of the horizon. A flapping overhead caught my attention and as I looked up I saw a majestic eagle flying low, sailing past lazily. "This is it," I said to myself. "This is the place," I smiled with joy.

"We are here," said Kahuna reading my thoughts and the others nodded in agreement. When I looked around I felt that everyone had identified with the place even before Kahuna said this was the spiritual ground we were looking for. I guess when we encounter the right partner, the right job, the right house, the right person, the right place, we instantly know. I guess that sometimes our heart is filled with so much pain and disappointment that our vision of what is ideal and perfect and spiritual gets blurred. Because we can't see it or feel it we feel we are not worthy of seeking or attaining it. But if we stick to the journey, one day we will step into that clearing where time lies still, where all is perfect, and our spirit will know that we have arrived. I had found the spiritual place for the sweat lodge. It was my finding. Kahuna had only acknowledged what my spirit had found first.

Kahuna walked a few steps towards the pond and stretched his arms out as though he was breathing in the energy of the pond. After a few seconds he turned around and beckoned the four men towards him. "Ten feet from here we build the fire pit," he instructed.

I stood by the wild flower bushes. Their fragrance was as wild as their colours and their presence. I didn't offer to help. I had learnt fast. Medicine men see help as interference in the process. If you are not the master or his disciple then you must only approach when you are invited.

"Observation is the best medium of learning," Kahuna had mentioned in our conversation earlier. "Observation puts the responsibility of learning on your shoulders. Your responsibility of learning is different from the teacher's responsibility of teaching. When you observe, you are your own teacher. You choose what you want to learn and you choose what to do with that learning." So I was content to observe and learn through my own force.

The four men opened a rucksack made of knitted fabric, like a medicine bag, and took out some tools. They began to systematically dig a hole at the point Kahuna had pointed out. They made a nice circular shape about two feet deep and three feet wide. One of the men got up, inspected his work and drew a large circle around the pit about fifteen feet in diameter. This would be the marking for the sweat lodge. Nine people would soon be huddled in a lodge fifteen feet in diameter.

Kahuna drew a line of about twenty feet from the centre of the sweat lodge marking, parallel to the pond. One of the men got up and began to dig a pit at the point where the line ended. "We will plant the tree of fulfilment here," Kahuna said. The second man brought a beautiful sapling of a sage tree and planted it in a mound in the pit his friend had freshly dug. In Northern Europe sage leaves are considered holy and sacred. They are dried and used in many spiritual rituals like we do in India.

I saw everyone had split up and was cutting branches in various directions. "Come help me carry this to the sweat lodge," Emma said. I helped carry the freshly cut branches. They were heavier than they seemed. Rick lined up the branches and began to build a sort of igloo keeping the fire pit at the centre. In less than thirty minutes he had single-handedly intertwined the branches making the skeleton of what looked like a wooden igloo.

Emma and Sain were carrying some black rocks over to where Rick had dug another pit vertically about twenty feet from the sweat lodge and had started a fire. These were volcanic rocks often used in prayers by the shamans. The volcanic rocks are amazing. When they are burning they are blood red in colour as though they are alive and when you take them off the fire a black layer of ash forms on them. "Don't be fooled by the ash, because the rock is alive inside," said Emma, explaining how travellers would mistake the live volcanic rocks for solid boulders and consequently burn to death. Things and situations are not what they sometimes seem. We are all travellers in life, moving on to uncharted boundaries in pursuit of our dreams. Knowledge, guidance and sheer presence of mind helps in unwanted heartbreaks and mishaps.

I could see the four medicine men walking in a row, each carrying a pile of thick blankets. In total silence they began to cover the wooden igloo with seven layers of thick blankets till what emerged was a very warm looking sweat lodge. The sweat lodge with blankets was tied up with ropes to prevent the blankets from falling or being swayed by the wind. A small opening was made on the side facing the freshly planted sage sapling. The sweat lodge was ready.

A figure in the distance caught my eye. A drop-dead gorgeous man, lean and muscular, was walking towards me. It was a scene straight out of a Tom Cruise film. He was dressed in blue jeans, a white shirt and black aviator sunglasses. I forgot all about my ailing heart. It was what my friends call "love at first sight".

As Martin came nearer, he waved. "I'm going to be the lodge keeper," he smiled. A lodge keeper is the person who is in charge of keeping the volcanic rocks burning outside and bringing them into the lodge at ceremonial intervals. He is the person who keeps the prayers "safe". I was happy to see Martin. He seemed like the perfect man for me except that I later found out he was engaged. I was curious to know what kind of woman it took to deserve a man like Martin. I would never find out. For now I was just happy that he was there.

"Let's start the ceremony! It's time!" Kahuna announced. "You can place your clothes and shoes by the bushes." He pointed towards the pond. Martin looked my way and smiled, and I smiled back. I unbuttoned my coat, not breaking eye contact. Martin's smile grew wider and I could see his shiny white teeth. "A perfect set of teeth," I said to myself. I took off my coat and placed it on the bush. When I turned around Martin was still looking my way. I blushed. I had a trick up my sleeve but I still found myself feeling bashful. I unbuttoned my shirt and pulled it over my shoulder to reveal my swimming costume underneath. Martin roared with laughter. "I don't believe you are actually going to wear your swimming costume," he said, laughing and shaking his head. "Yes I am!" I smiled back. I guess I had still not made peace with the effortless nudity around. I was tolerant of

other people's beliefs and cultures and they were tolerant
of mine. It was harmony amidst diversity. I have continued
to practise that long after the sweat lodge, to allow people
to be! Ever since the sweat lodge I have never found the
need to change others or their opinions, and more than that
I have never needed to impose my beliefs and values on
others. There is only one right thing to do and that is what
YOU think is the right thing to do. We learn and we change
and we grow, and that is more of an internal trigger than an
external force.

We sat down in a circle on the cold, wet grass. Kahuna was
semi-naked, wearing a thick, red and white woollen garment
around his waist. He had a very sturdy body—he looked like
the kind of yogi you find up in the Himalayas. He was one
of those timeless kinds of people. The four medicine men,
Rick, and Sain sat down on either side of Kahuna in their
birthday suits, stark naked. I think I had an influence on
Emma because she sat beside me with her bathing suit on.
No one was looking at anyone. Everyone was self involved,
getting ready for the ritual. Kahuna started the chant and
everyone joined in. I remained silent.

As the chanting grew, I was surprised I was not in prayer
mode. I was just there. I was present. I was aware. Just days
before, I had arrived in the Netherlands in a confused state
of mind and now my home, the pain, the despair, my broken
relationship, the nagging voices, the uncaring demands,
all seemed like a bad dream. In that moment I could not
relate to the life that I had been living just two days prior.
My thirty years of chaos and confusion were turned upside
down, dried and cleaned up; as though I had "laundered"
the memory of all that I had left behind.

Suddenly I felt that in spirit I had conspired against my
stupid self to create the mess that I found myself in, so that
I would move beyond it to seek. I felt that I had led myself
here. All of a sudden all the events in my life, even the most

unpleasant ones, made sense. If my life had not been a mess, I would not be here. We seek in times of turbulence. Peace brings static. I could hear the chants growing in intensity. I didn't know whether the thoughts crossing my mind were right or wrong but I sure knew they were important. If I was responsible for being here, for being a part of this amazing spiritual process, then I was also responsible for the pain and hardship that I had caused myself just weeks ago. If my spirit had grown in merely one day of spiritual exposure, then even the mess that I had caused was my spirit's will. And if I saw my life as one long path then every "bad experience" created was a movement towards the "good experience" that followed. I realised that by taking creative responsibility for the bad, I ensured the occurrence of the good.

The chanting ended abruptly; at least that's what I thought. The dialect was foreign to me, and the beginning and the end sounded no different.

"Now is the time to bring forth your heart's desire," Kahuna said, marking the end of the chanting ritual. I saw everyone move into prayer mode, legs crossed, palms up. I followed.

"Think about your heart's desire. Desire is your soul's plan for you to discover yourself. Desire is your soul's plan to grow. Desire is your prayer. Desire is not something that is sinful. When you meet your heart's desire there is beauty and abundance. That is the true state of being. It is desire that puts your soul into action for its manifestation. Desire is soul play. Indulge! There are no limits," Kahuna said in a prayer-like recital.

What was my heart's desire? Not a single thought crossed my mind. I had just been through hell and back. My dreams had been broken, my bank balance had been zeroed, I had lost everything. I was broken. What desire can a broken being have? How can one desire in a state of hopelessness? It cannot happen. The two can't live in the same heart. I now understood why people succumb deeper to depression in setbacks when you show them the path to success. I understood why people won't bank on hope when their hearts are in despair. I could clearly see why people crumble with fear when you talk about their dreams. Desire is a foreign idea to someone who is in despair. Desire is a rude joke for someone who has not yet moved beyond pain. The one advantage that I had over every other lost soul was that I had left my world behind, literally. I began to think . . . of a new world.

I wanted everything. I desired all the goodness the world had to offer. I wanted abundance at its fullest. I wanted wealth in all its sanity. I wanted fame in all its glory. I desired the soul mate I had so longed for. I desired a beautiful family. I desired more opportunities to express my talent. I desired the best experiences possible on planet earth. I desired to be one with the creator. I desired to expand with the universe, to grow beyond the boundaries of growth. I desired love with no conditions. I desired love without restriction, love for the sake of love. I wanted everything.

As I opened my eyes I saw everyone staring at me. They watched me with eager, loving eyes, patiently waiting for me to finish. I was ignited. I was alive. I was home.

Kahuna got up and so did everyone else, palms still open in prayer. I was excited. My heart raced and my legs trembled, as though I was going to enter my dream life that very moment. "We will now plant something that symbolises your heart's desire under and around the sage sapling. Anything that you feel summarises what you want, plant it with this holy herb and may your desires find the most spiritually uplifting way to manifest into your lives. May your desire be an answer to the world's prayer!"

We walked towards the sage sapling in a row.

Rick took out his arm band and began to dig it into the soil around the sage tree. Emma took out her necklace and got in line to plant her desire. Suddenly Sain took off towards the cottage. He obviously wanted to get something to plant. If Sain could go, I could too, I thought. After all I hadn't brought anything to offer. I followed on Sain's trail, my legs shivering and my face suddenly pierced with the cold breeze. My feet went numb on the cold grass but the excitement to design a whole new life carried me determinedly to the cottage. I saw Sain dash out as speedily as he had entered. He was quick at what he wanted. The door was still swinging as I entered the cottage. I walked into the room and opened my rucksack. What could I possibly offer as a symbol of my desires?

My hands were trembling and I knew it was not due to the cold. It was the sheer thrill of being alive. Of suddenly having found the capacity to desire and to dare to design a beautiful world for myself. It was also the delight of knowing I could now do it with awareness.

I pulled out my favourite t-shirt and my Tissot watch, my only designer watch. I took out my debit card, some money, my butterfly necklace, and my white gold ring. I even took out the boarding pass of my flight to the Netherlands, my company brochure, my business card, my family picture, my diary, and a small idol of Ganesha. I wrapped them all in my t-shirt and ran back, hoping that the ritual would not be over by the time I reached.

Everyone was waiting for me by the sage sapling. I had expected Martin to break into laughter looking at the stuff I was carrying. I was half expecting Kahuna to give me a weary look for all the insignificant "material" that I had brought forth. But no one said a word. No one had any reaction or any expression of censure. I think the judgement about my action was in my head alone. We all judge our own words, actions and intentions and then assume that others judge us in the same way. We kid ourselves by worrying about what "they" would think of us. "They" are another "us" and are thinking the same thing. So there is a planet full of people thinking what others would think about them and losing out on their own thought for their own life and purpose. My load of "symbols" of my desires made no difference to anyone.

I meticulously dug several holes around the sapling. With my debit card I expressed my desire for financial abundance; with my watch, timeless joy and timeless happiness. As I dug a big hole for my company brochure and business card I let loose my desire for abundant opportunities and infinite glory. I put in my white gold ring for beauty, and my butterfly necklace for freedom. I put in the hundred rupee note and my t-shirt, picturing absolute abundance. I planted my gratitude diary and knew that I would be blessed with wisdom to live life to the fullest. And finally I planted Ganesha with the desire that I could call upon him in the future for more desires. I had just begun after all. I like to keep the door to goodness always slightly ajar so that I can find my way back in. I am a total crook; I will steal any goodness I can, right under the Lord's nose as well.

I was not in a hurry. I took my time to visualise, to feel, to touch every little feeling, and the joy that overflowed was divine. It was as though my desires had been granted. It was as though my life until now didn't matter. What mattered was "now" and what was to come. I was excited to live the rest of my life because my choice was made. I was looking forward to living my life as I saw fit. And it was an amazingly uplifting feeling. I felt like a designer, an artist, putting colours and shapes and character into my own life. I felt like a true creator.

I finally got up and dusted my hands to get the mud off. I was grinning from ear to ear. I was happy for no reason at all. My hands were still covered with mud as I brought them together in prayer. But I didn't care.

We all formed a circle around the sapling. Martin brought some simmering sage leaves and dusted us all with the incense of the fumes. He had a sort of fan made of owl feathers and waved it up and down over everyone in strokes as though he was repainting a new aura around us. The gentle breeze and the whisk of the feathers made me feel as though a lot of clearing up was taking place in my space for real. The scent of the simmering sage leaves filled the air and even the birds in the vicinity quietened down as an acknowledgement of the spiritual process.

"The rocks are ready," Martin said to Kahuna, placing the simmering leaves on a coral shell next to the sage sapling.

Kahuna turned towards us and explained, "The sweat lodge is a spiritual ceremony. While inside we will be performing four phases of prayers. Every phase will mark the opening of the sweat lodge. The volcanic rocks will be replaced by fresh burning rocks which Martin will pass. Every phase is an opportunity for you to step out of the sweat lodge if you feel you want to. Once the prayers start you cannot under any circumstance leave. Are there any questions?" I had no questions. I was too excited.

Sain entered the lodge first. He crept into the small opening. Martin had opened one part of the blanket which formed a sort of entrance. The four medicine men followed. Emma entered next and I prepared to go in after her. As I moved to the entrance of the sweat lodge, I turned back to see the sage sapling. My desires would now be my prayer. I turned to Martin who was holding the blanket up for me. He smiled and I dropped to my knees to creep in.

I could not see anything inside the sweat lodge. It was dark and cramped. "Come this side," I heard Sain say. People had to sit equally on both sides, huddled together. I sat next to Sain. One of the medicine men was sitting in front of me. There was hardly any place and I had to squeeze right next to him. I folded my legs towards my chest and held them with my arms. The grass was wet and I could swear I felt something creep up my legs. I took a deep breath and tried to get the crawling feeling out of my head. I was uncomfortable.

Rick and Kahuna entered. I kept my eyes towards the entrance, which was the only source of light. The inside of the sweat lodge was very dim and my eyes strained to adjust. It was as though I was desperately trying to see. We are so dependent on our senses for security and orientation that when one sense is diminished it causes stress mentally and physically. I could feel the mental havoc that the darkness was bringing with it.

The flap of the sweat lodge opened and Martin rolled in a big volcanic rock balanced on two metal forks. It brought instant warmth into the lodge. The rock was gleaming red, giving the lodge a night lamp glow. "Any light was better than darkness," I thought. The flap opened again and in came another rock, followed by five more. Once all the rocks were inside, Martin announced that the sweat lodge would be closed.

The entrance to the lodge was sealed with the flap of the blanket. The redness of the rocks dimmed and died out in less than two minutes. This was the first time I was exposed to total and absolute darkness. I struggled for some light. There was none. It was pitch-dark. There was nothing, only darkness. There was no point keeping my eyes open any more. Either way there was only darkness. I closed my eyes.

I forgot who was on my sides. I forgot who I was huddled against. There was silence and there was darkness. No one spoke. I guess this was the time for adjustment. This was the time to make peace with where you were. Suddenly the creepy crawlies on my legs had disappeared. Who was next to me did not matter. Slowly, the sensation of my body also disappeared. There was a vacuum, nothingness. I thought of the stories of captivity one reads about prisoners in dark cells, except here it was voluntary. This was self-imprisonment with a purpose.

Time was irrelevant. I realised that awareness IS, it never WAS and never WILL BE. Awareness is in the present state. And the only time that was real was NOW. If I were to craft my watch, every minute and every hour would be marked NOW. I had never been in a state where the past did not exist for me. But now, all that mattered was NOW.

If at that moment you were to ask me who I was, I would not have known. I had lost all sense of identity. There was a feeling of blankness, as though who I had become, was not who I really wanted to be. Who I was, was who I had become as a result of circumstance. And now was my opportunity to discover myself and to be it.

A loud hiss yanked me out of my thoughts. Kahuna, I assumed it was Kahuna, splashed a handful of water on the volcanic rocks and at once there was vapour and heat and a loud hiss. Kahuna started to chant alone. He explained that the rocks would emit heat and he would continuously splash water on the rocks to stir up vapour. This vapour is inhaled and absorbed by the skin and has medicinal and healing benefits. It heals chronic and rheumatic illnesses, chronic aches and pains and also purifies and detoxifies the skin and the system.

I inhaled the vapour for a while and then I began to get uncomfortable with the heat. There was no ventilation. It was stuffy. It was hot and sweaty. For a second I thought, "I want to go out" but I quickly changed the thought to "I want to be here. I have brought myself here."

Kahuna continued to chant alone. His voice was deep and resonating. It seemed as though he was going into a trance.

By now I had lost all sensation of my body. My body did not exist. There was only awareness; a blinking, living awareness that was witnessing it all.

Kahuna spoke, "We are now invoking the spirits of the four directions. These are the guardians of our planet. We will invoke them to remind and direct us to our true purpose, without which we are confused, lost cogs deluding others by our mere presence. The spirits of the four directions will awaken in us our forgotten purpose as a result of which we have misled ourselves into believing we are perishable beings. We are points of intention; we are expansive, ever growing spirits. We lose that power and become destructible points and sources when we have no direction or purpose. A being with a purpose is a universal force. A being with a purpose is divinity in action. You will become what you experience as god."

Kahuna then held up a "talking stick" and rattled it.

"Talking stick?" I thought. This would be something, to hear what a stick had to say.

"The talking stick is made of a cat's leg with a monkey's skull on the top. The monkey's skull is skinned together with some small pieces of bone in the hollow," Kahuna explained. When he shook the stick, it rattled. I winced at the thought of killing animals but it was a comforting feeling to know that the talking stick was made out of dead animals and was used for spiritual rituals.

"I will pass the stick to you one by one. Rattle the stick and it will talk to you. It will tell you your life's purpose. Once the stick has finished its message, rattle it again and pass it on. Once all the members of the lodge have been ignited to their purpose, we will end phase one with a prayer." With this, Kahuna and the others started the prayer. It was a trance-like prayer and I felt that the spirits were really being woken up from their slumber. The prayer was made up of a lot of hums, some short, some extended.

The chant ended and Kahuna rattled the stick. He still spoke in a hum-like dialect, "The talking stick has been invoked." I felt something touch my head but before I could let out a shriek, Kahuna said, "The talking stick has chosen its first partner."

I felt his hand take mine and thrust the talking stick into it. "Here," he said. I was shocked.

Talking stick? I did not know how to use it. I was waiting to witness someone else's purpose unfold first. I needed an example. I was new and had never done this before. I was freaking out. I did not know what to do with the talking stick. Suddenly, panic engulfed me. I had felt this panic before. It was the panic of responsibility without experience. It was the panic of responsibility without guidance. It was as though I had been put on the race track at the Olympics for the hundred meter sprint. I began protesting, "There has been a mistake!"

But the sweat lodge is not a place for protests; it is a place for purpose. I was the chosen one. There had to be a reason for me to be the first. Just moments before, the realisation had dawned that everything that had happened in my life was driven by one purpose: to bring me to where I was at that point. This too was a part of that purpose. I had to trust my own realisation. I had to put faith in my own knowing and bet on my own young wisdom to rattle the stick and allow it to talk to me and unfold my purpose.

I stopped my mental chatter and rattled the stick. I waited.

The stick was silent. "Maybe I didn't rattle it right," I thought. I waited some more. The stick was silent. I rattled it again. Nothing. Mere silence. "Maybe I don't have a purpose," I thought. "Maybe I was a mistake, like my mom once told me. Maybe I was not worth the purpose." I could feel myself sinking into a pit of worthlessness. I rattled the stick pleadingly. It remained silent. "Maybe I am not ready for my purpose. Maybe I am too young. Maybe women are not meant to be awakened to their purpose. Maybe it is the illness that I went through as a child. Maybe it is due to my past life sins. Maybe I am not a good daughter." I found my self-worth being systematically reduced until I ran out of reasons for being unfit to recognise my purpose. The stick stayed stubbornly silent. It did not want to talk to me.

Then Kahuna began to hum. It was the same trance hum from the chant. A few more voices joined in the humming and I rattled the stick again.

And suddenly, stick in hand, I spoke as though from somewhere outside my body.

"I was meant to heal people. I was meant to reach out to the entire world, to touch their lives with my spiritual evolution. I was meant to shine and radiate my light with hope and direction to heal the hearts of those who have stopped believing in themselves. I was meant to be a messenger of joy, of happiness, of abundance. I was meant to be the guardian of goodness, of kindness and of dignity. My purpose is to bring love and peace through my words, actions and intention. It is my purpose to communicate clearly and to use my life in service of the highest good for the highest number of purposes that there ever will be. I will measure the worth of my life with the quality of the world that I leave behind. I will live in love and that will be my identity for the world to know. I have found my purpose. I have found myself."

I rattled the stick and passed it to the person next to me. Kahuna and the others started to hum. It was a faster hum, as though celebrating a person who has found herself after having long been lost.

I don't know what Sain spoke. I don't know what anyone else spoke. My voice, my purpose, and the vision of that purpose took form right before my eyes.

Cats do not talk, neither do monkey heads. But when put on the spot to find your purpose with time standing still in your hand, with no other option other than choosing your purpose, you will certainly find it. Anyone will. All my life I had escaped from reality. I had allowed myself to flee to avoid looking at what I was really here for. I had ample opportunities to look within but I would always sneak out from the back door.

Today with the talking stick in my hand, with no option but to find my purpose, I found it. Trust me, there was no escape. The rocks were smouldering, the vapour was steaming the body, there were eight other people waiting in line—I had no option but to find my purpose.

The myth says that the talking stick talks. Actually the talking stick is a stick of responsibility; when it comes into your hand you have to take responsibility for your life and destiny. And if there was really a stick that spoke then I had heard it talk a million times in the voices of my mother, father, teacher, and the thousands I had encountered. It was when I followed their talk to my destiny that I messed myself up. Today was MY TALK. It was MY PURPOSE. It was MY SPIRIT alone. There was no past. There was no reference other than now.

I could hear the hum and the rattle, the hiss and the voices. I was rejoicing in the discovery people were making for themselves. The darkness had unfolded several scenes. I could see, literally see, my whole life unfold. The kind of life you read about in fairy tales, the kind of life one writes about, the kind of life that is an invitation to divinity. I could see every day as a blessing, as a discovery of my true self. I could see growth, mentally and spiritually. I could see peace. I could see service. I could see abundance. I could see joy. It was the perfect life. I knew I had arrived at that recognition. I knew I had awakened to the power to create it. And I knew this was me.

I don't know how much time passed. I knew the spirits of the four directions were alive. They were witness to my purpose and would guide me and protect me everywhere I went. The hum stopped. The heat grew. Kahuna spoke, "The first prayer is over. We will change the rocks and start again. Now is the opportunity for you to step out should you want to. Does anyone want to step out?"

No one answered. I wanted to go out. Suddenly I realised how hot and stuffy it was. Suddenly I wanted to run out and meet the world. I was a woman on fire. I wanted to go out and breathe fresh air and dance with abandon. I waited for someone else to take the initiative. No one did. I felt uncomfortable. If only someone would volunteer to go out first! When Sain had rushed to the cottage to get symbols of his desire I had darted out too. I don't know if I would have done that if I had not seen Sain do it. I usually wait for someone else to make the first move, even if I badly want to do something myself. I don't want to risk looking foolish and if I must then I must at least have company. I acknowledged this thought and decided I would break it. I would take the risk of being foolish alone. I would take the risk of venturing out alone even if no one else joined me.

Martin opened the flap of the sweat lodge and astoundingly beautiful rays of sunlight came flooding in. At that point I realised my eyes were still closed. When I opened my eyes I could see red hot gleaming rocks and the flap was shut again. "Oh no," I thought. But a few seconds later the flap opened again and on the fork were three medium sized rocks. As Kahuna helped Martin put the rocks in the pit I spoke up, "I would like to step out for some time." I took the risk of being the only one into the "unknown".

Kahuna looked in my direction and said, "That's great." Martin opened the flap and I had to drag myself out. My legs were almost frozen together.

I stepped out in the light and it pierced my eyes. I was blinded with the sudden exposure to light. I could not see. This is the phase called "temporary blindness" when one moves from darkness to light. When you make a sudden shift in your world or your perspective, there is this phase of temporary confusion. But if you just hold on to the determination of taking that leap, the blindness and confusion will pass and a beautiful world will unfold before your eyes. But many of us freak out in this stage of temporary confusion and run back to our familiar world of darkness without giving the light a chance to grow on us.

I covered my eyes with my hands and stood still. A few moments later I slowly opened my eyes, squinting at first and then embracing the light. The sight was beautiful. The whole expanse was radiant. The sky was a blue I had never seen before. The sun was faint and friendly. Birds chirped, eagles flew low, frogs hopped into the pond and dragonflies celebrated the day. It was wonderful. I was so happy. I was sweaty and hot and the cool breeze and fresh air was all I needed before I went in again.

"Do you want to take a dip in the pond?" Martin asked, lifting the last few volcanic rocks. I thought he must have been out of his mind but I did not bother saying it. I continued to fill my lungs with light and life before getting back into the sweat lodge.

A few seconds passed and I heard Martin's voice. "Ok, we are closing the lodge," he said, putting down the flaps of the blankets.

"Wait," I screamed and ran towards the entrance. Martin caught my arm as I almost tripped. "You can't go back in once you are out!"

I was shocked. "What? How can you do that? I took Kahuna's permission to step out. In fact Kahuna asked if anyone wanted to step out," I protested.

The fact that I secretly admired Martin went diving in the pond; I would fight the man if I had to. I wanted to get back into the sweat lodge before the second prayer started. "You can't go back once you are out," Martin repeated calmly, totally ignoring my passionate outburst.

"But he didn't tell me that," I said, pointing towards Kahuna who was in the dark lodge.

"You should have asked and clarified before you left," Martin retorted calmly, putting down the last flap.

I felt like a lost girl. Like someone who had missed her train, the last train, back home. It felt unfair, just like when my boyfriend left me for another woman. It felt cold and bitter, just like when no one stood by my side in my despair. I felt cheated, just like I did when my friends who knew about the other woman never told me. "You never asked," the y said.

I was lost right after having found my purpose. I was angry and started to walk back to the cottage with tears welling up in my eyes.

Martin ran up to me and held my arm firmly, totally ignoring my emotional eruption. "You can't go. You have to be here outside the lodge until the end of the ritual. You are still IN the prayer. It's just that you are OUT."

I didn't know which was worse, not being in the lodge or having to sit out in 2°C of freezing cold in my bathing suit.

I didn't say a word. I sat on a tree stump that Martin offered me right next to the lodge. I could feel the warmth of the volcanic rocks and the blankets from inside the lodge. I sat on the stump shivering violently, my teeth chattering, and tears rolling down my cheeks.

Martin was tending the stones in the fire pit. My misery did not bother him. He was at peace with his task. "I can't carry your problem into my duties," he seemed to convey silently.

I could hear the hum inside the sweat lodge and I broke into a sob. I felt Martin's hand on my shoulder. It was warm from the fire. He got his tree stump next to mine and sat down. He took my hand in his and waited till I raised my eyes and looked into his. Clear blue. He was so saint-like, so young, so my kind of man. "If you hurt your hand and I put some medicine on it, it will heal. But what would happen if, after it heals, I continue to put the medicine on your hand?" he asked.

"That would make it worse," I answered.

"Exactly. You needed what you got. That was enough for your healing. Your spirit knows how much you need. And you left. Some people heal faster than others; some people need more medicine than others do. You got what you needed. Trust the process."

"But I wanted to be in. I wanted to learn more," I still protested.

"There is no in, there is no out. There is only here. Your best lesson is learnt 'here' and the here is where you are now."

His hand still held mine and I pondered over his words. I was cold and shivering. I thought of the warmth inside the sweat lodge. At that instant a fat green frog hopped out into the open and headed straight for the pond. In one giant leap he made a splash and majestically swam across, leaving a long trail in the water. The frog was out in the freezing cold. It was the kind of frog you find in your backyard during the monsoon. Not a special pedigree to survive the cold. I could see the larks perched on the trees, the dragon flies making circles in the grass, the flowers blooming with joy. Everything in nature seemed at peace with the cold except me.

When I was in the warmth inside the lodge, I wanted to be in the cold outside. Now that I was outside in the cold, I wanted to be back in the warmth. This to and fro journey never ends. And the worst is that even though I was spending time and covering distance, I was really not getting anywhere. When I was in a relationship I wanted to be single. When I was single I so badly wanted to be in a relationship. When I was working insane hours, I wanted time out. When I had the time out, I wanted to get back to work. There is something beyond this meaningless travel to nowhere, there is something beyond here and there, and that is acceptance of where you are now. I was out in the cold; so be it. I could experience it. I didn't have to make an emotional crisis out of my experience. The frog was living in sanity and I was making my life hell.

The minute I allowed myself to experience the cold, to be in the moment, to be a part of the cold, I stopped feeling it. The cold was no longer foreign or something to be avoided. It became me.

"Do you want to take a dip in the pond?" Martin asked again. "That usually completes the sweat lodge ritual. If you want to that is!" I looked at him and smiled.

I walked towards the pond "How deep is it?" I asked.

"Enough for you to wade in," he shouted back.

I stood where the frog had leapt off and jumped into the pond screaming like a little girl.

The water was muddy and ice cold. I ruffled up its surface as I jumped in. I splashed around for a few seconds and came out dripping. I was a shade of red and white. I think my blood was confused, not knowing whether to freeze or to flow, leaving patches of red and white confusion. But I felt a rejuvenation I had never felt before. From boiling heat to freezing cold; I had shocked my body to life. It was as though my body hosted a dormant spirit that was shaken alive.

I walked towards the stump. I WAS the cold. I was no longer feeling cold. I could feel the breeze in my wet hair but it wasn't a painful cold breeze. I guess acceptance and tolerance frees you from the burden of pain even if it is physical. I often wondered how war captives endure torture and still refuse to talk. They make peace with the pain and it cannot break them. All my life I had given pain a run and it always caught up with me. I never stood still in the face of all that was wrong. I never experienced it with the grace of the frog jumping into the pond.

I looked back on my life and figured in all honesty that if I were to relive all that had gone wrong, if I were to live through all the pain I had in my life, I would do it with grace and dignity. And I guess when you experience life with grace and dignity, pain withdraws immediately. If you are ready to face it then it cannot be painful. It is painful when you avoid it. An experience is painful if it is perceived as such. For the frogs the pond is full of water to rejoice; warm or cold is a circumstance. The same applies to our lives. The option to play is ours. That day I chose to play. From that day on, no matter what my circumstance, I would play and I would be happy.

Martin sat beside me the whole time, passing rocks in the intervals and sometimes even humming along with the group inside.

"Hold their prayers, bless their prayers," is what Martin would occasionally tell me. I felt powerful sitting outside the sweat lodge guarding people's prayers including mine.

"You don't need permission to empower people. You don't need permission to bless. That is your soul extending its love and joy by including others in its well being. To wish well for another is an act of an enlightened soul. Remember your spirit. Bless and rejoice at every opportunity," Martin explained.

The last hum ended and the last rattle faded. Martin opened the flaps of the lodge. Kahuna appeared first, his body blood red. The medicine men crawled out crimson-skinned and dripping with sweat. Emma, Rick and Sain followed suit. Once out, all of them headed for the pond and dived in, screaming, laughing and rejoicing.

I looked at Martin. "The ritual is complete," he smiled.

As the group splashed around in the pond, I helped Martin pack the lava rocks in the fire pit. He collected some ash in his hand. "Here, take this. Let this remind you that you are bigger than you can imagine, that you are in good hands with yourself, that you can if you will it, that your desires will be the answer to the world's prayers."

I took the ash and wrapped it in the old newspaper Martin had used to light up the fire pit.

I collected my coat and clothes and had no urge to slip them on. I walked in my bathing suit in 2°C temperature, perfectly content in the experience of life.

As I entered the cottage Mary exclaimed, "The dishes are on you tonight, lass. You didn't make your bed." I smiled. "Bring it on. I can do them tomorrow too." I knew I would enjoy washing the dishes as much as I would have enjoyed my night out under the stars. There is nowhere but here, and I was here.

I went for a bath not caring about the door anymore. It was strange that when I stopped worrying about it, no one bothered me either. We create our own realities. I clearly understood the meaning of "what you resist persists". By not resisting, I had released that event from my life. I had an amazing "fear free" bath with hot water. While everyone was chatting excitedly in the room, sharing their experiences of the sweat lodge, I slipped under the sheets and smiled into infinity. My purpose was clear. My life awaited me.

I dozed off to sleep knowing I would be woken in time for dinner and dishes.

My experiences 'lessoned' for you:

···> It's ok to feel lost and confused. It's ok that you don't know what you want. When you encounter the right person, the right place, the right job, you will instantly know. Keep looking.

···> There is only one right thing to do and that is what you believe to be right. There is no need to change other people's opinion. They have a right to their growth and self discovery as much as you do.

···> The bad is an opportunity for the occurrence of the good. That is the cycle. Every sunset marks the certainty of sunrise. If there is bad, then good is a certain next.

···> Desire is the soul's yearning to turn thoughts into experiences. Desire puts your life into action for its manifestation.

···> Desire is the fastest cure for despair. Dare to dream when you are in despair and you will rise up like the phoenix from the ashes.

···> The one thing worse than judging another is judging what others will think about you. Both don't matter.

···> There is no limit to what you want. Desire has no rules or boundaries.

···> We con ourselves into believing that we are lost. If you will yourself to find your purpose and leave no option but to find it, you will discover it for yourself.

···> Your destiny is your path, you don't wait for others to step up first. You are the only one who can take the initiative for your own destiny. Step up.

···> It's futile to compare yourself with others. It's futile to protest against circumstance. There is only one place you are meant to be and that place is "here". Your lesson is best learnt at only one time and that is "now".

···> Grace and dignity is the answer to all pain that there is. When dignity and grace define your experience of the world, there is no pain.

The Salt Cleanse

I heard the alarm and wished it was not time to rise and shine. I was not done sleeping. In fact it felt as though I had just fallen asleep. I half opened an eyelid and pressed "snooze". I could hear doors opening and closing, and snatches of chatter between Emma and Sain, but I managed to sleep through it all.

The alarm rang again persistently but I still wasn't ready. I pressed "dismiss" and woke up angrily as though doing the world a favour. I got up and almost bumped into Rick, a towel around his waist and dripping water. "Watch it, lady, else it will be the full monty this morning."

I smiled it off. "Good morning," I muttered and headed for the bath. It was steaming from the hot shower that Rick had just got out of. I undressed and entered the shower. I love the feeling of water on my face, it always wakes me up.

"There is a morning bathing ritual," I heard Rick's voice behind me as I turned in circles trying to hide myself. Rick opened the glass door of the shower and stepped in four feet away from me. I was dumbfounded. I was naked in the shower and this gigantic half-naked creature was going to teach me a morning ritual for which I had not enrolled! Rick stepped closer. He held my face, the water still dripping down my head, and pulled me closer to him.

"Nooooooooooooooo," I screamed, as the sound of the alarm ripped through my dream. I opened my eyes and saw my phone flashing options "snooze" or "dismiss". I dismissed it with all my might and jumped up, wide awake. Phew! It was just a dream! My brain was playing tricks on me to watch me jump out of bed. "Serves me right!" I muttered to myself.

"Hey, it's a happy morning," Rick said, bending towards me and sitting on my bed. I cringed, my dream still fresh in my head. The water from his hair dripped on my blanket but he didn't seem to care.

"Today is the Salt Cleanse ritual. It's a spiritual challenge. Like an arm wrestle with who you think you are and who you really are. Many people fail the test. You are not a native, you are a city girl. Even if you fail, remember that no one expects you to pass, so don't be disappointed." Rick spoke with the warmth of a person who cared for me. He didn't know me but he cared. The image of Rick as a serial rapist soon left my mind and I was at ease. But I was a little uncomfortable at the thought of the spiritual challenge. I love challenges. I'm a person who creates challenges in the simplest of the tasks. I guess the joys of victory and growth happen only when you move beyond yourself and overcome challenges.

I didn't like the disclaimer though: "Many people fail the test and you are not expected to pass." Why do people fail? I have never understood failure. In attempting any task there is fear of failure, hanging overhead like a double edged sword, mocking you in anticipation of your defeat.

If I did not pass the Salt Cleanse ritual, I would not be able to attend any other ritual. The shaman's rituals were for spiritual freedom for spiritual purposes. I wanted to be free. I was sincerely lost. I had confessed to myself that I was lost, I didn't know what I wanted, I didn't know what was right anymore, I didn't know where I was going. I was lost. I was so lost that I was losing faith in myself and in my ability to do the right thing. I was looking at this week of rituals as an opportunity to live again, fully. And now there was this heavily built "don't mess with me" bouncer at the door, asking for my entry pass—the "Salt Cleanse Pass" stamp.

What could be the challenge? Whom did I have to fight against? What did I have to win over? What were the rules? Under what conditions did one fail? What was needed to pass? At least someone should have told me that so I could be prepared. I hated this "secret" about everything. If I did not know the rules then how could I prepare myself to win?

I didn't know the rules for a relationship and I had lost. I didn't know the rules for business and I had lost. I didn't know the rules for anything about life and I was losing big time. If only someone had told me the rules to create a beautiful relationship I would have done everything in my power to create one. If someone had just told me the rules for building a solid professional empire, I would have expended my energy day and night in building it. But no one told me. I guess no one knew. I guess each one of us is on a personal journey to achieve victory and grieve over failure because both are individual perspectives.

When I broke up with my boyfriend, most of my friends said, "You are lucky this happened now. You are lucky you found out the truth at this stage. You are lucky you did not get married." But no matter how much good fortune they bestowed upon me, I knew I had failed. I had been headed in a certain direction, focussing all my energy there and life had turned me around and placed me on a different path. It was only when I turned around and looked at the reality I was creating that I realised it was a lie. Failure, to me, was spending two years of my life serving a man who was not worthy of my love. I could have put my time to better use. Failure, to me, was planning a future, moving closer to it every day, with a man who was not mine. I had failed.

I don't like failure.

Rick's words rang in my head as I slowly indulged in a hot

rejuvenating bath. Instead of the usual soap I found some bath salts placed in the bathroom. The feel of the coarse salts on my skin was divine. I felt really great. I was looking forward to the salt cleanse. I would survive the spiritual challenge.

I came down to the breakfast room, my skin still tingling from the salts. "There is only juice for breakfast today, carrot juice," Mary smiled. "There will be no more food for the day," she winked, raising her hands, pretending to be relieved not to cook for the day. I really liked Mary, not only because she was a great cook but also because she really cooked with interest and love. That was what made her bland food so delicious.

"Okayyyy," I thought to myself. No food would be a tough one. Although I come from a land where fasting is a major component of spiritual and religious rituals, I cannot fast for the love of god. I love food. I will succumb and die if I have to fast. I could already see the smirk on the face of Failure: "You will fail the test."

I drank the carrot juice slowly, pretending to fill my stomach up with that one glass of weird tasting juice. I began to think of all the war victims in the concentration camps who had to survive on just two tablespoons of soup a day. I suddenly sat up straight. What if I was a war victim and had no choice but to consume only two tablespoons of soup a day? What would I do? Would I commit suicide because I didn't get three meals a day? Sometimes life is tough, sometimes there is not enough, sometimes you have to accommodate and lie low. Sometimes the enemy is too strong and sometimes you have to give in today to get out tomorrow. I had been a brat all my life. It was either my way or the high way. And when people took the high way, I lost. It is like saying that you either give me a whole bowl of soup or take away these two spoons. The world would laugh at my foolishness.

But now I had new power. I was awakened. If it was only this carrot juice for the day, so be it. I would survive. I got up and walked out.

"The ritual is in the barn," Mary shouted at my back.

I already felt good. I was ready for any challenge. Failure was not an option. I would make it through.

I entered the barn. Emma had cleared the whole barn which smelt of chicken although none were in sight. Kahuna was sitting on a chair in conversation with Sain. I sat on an empty chair. It was a good thing they didn't ask us to sit on the ground; it was covered with fresh chicken poop!

There was a long table on the side with aluminium jugs and glasses. "We are going to have a party in the barn," I chuckled to myself.

"There you are," Kahuna said, standing up as he noticed me. "Welcome to the Salt Cleanse ritual. In some cultures it is also known as the Spiritual Challenge. Not everyone makes it to the other side simply because not everyone is ready to make the transition. Everyone has their own time and process of growth. Just like a five year old girl cannot lift the weight of an oversized suitcase, some people have not yet evolved to take the weight of this test. Failing the test does not make you good or bad, it just indicates that you are not yet ready and that there will be another time."

I nodded. I understood. I didn't know if I was ready but I knew I was willing and that is about as ready as you can get.

"Before you can cleanse your spirit, you need to cleanse your body. A healthy spirit after all resides in a healthy body. If you mess up your body, you will eventually mess up your spirit," Kahuna explained as he began to stride around the barn and I had to twist my neck around to follow him.

"The jugs contain the salt water. It is thick and some find it difficult to consume. It contains salts that will fish out the last morsel stuck in the folds of your intestines or even the bottom of your stomach. Most diseases start from the stomach. If your stomach and intestines host uncleared food particles they eventually grow toxic and disease is born. The salt will clear up your system, something like spring cleaning your body. Most of us take great care to clean our bodies on the outside as a daily ritual but never clean our bodies from the inside," Kahuna continued.

The mention of the body cleaning process transported me to the nightmare I had earlier of Rick engaging me in a taboo ritual and my thoughts went into disarray. Distraction is the onset of failure. I re-focussed on Kahuna; I was not going to fail.

"The salt will move in your body all the way from your mouth to your anal canal and out, bringing out all the crap that your body has stored. You will be around the barn. On the outside there are cubicles you will use to excrete when you feel the pressure build up. There are small metal containers outside the cubicle in which you will excrete. On the way out, you will close the lid and place the container in the corner assigned to you. Is this clear? You drink the salt and you poop, simple." Kahuna looked around and smiled.

I nodded in slight disgust. Yes, I drink and I poop, everyday, but it is never a public agenda let alone a ritual. But this was a spiritual challenge and I knew that passing this one would be a piece of cake. Drink and poop, and you pass.

Everyone got up and moved to the table. Emma lifted a jug and poured out a glass of salt drink. I watched her face as she took the first sip. No expression. It was a slow gulp. Her lips reached for another and she caught me eyeing her cautiously. She stopped in the middle of a gulp, raising her eyebrow as if to say, "Get on with your glass and don't stare at me." I smiled apologetically, lifted the half-filled jug and poured out the glass of salt water that would eventually change my life.

I raised the glass and brought it to my nose. I have a bad habit of first smelling everything I consume. The water was thick and translucent like corn soup with no pieces of corn in it. It smelt salty. I brought the glass to my lips and took a small sip and almost spat it out. It tasted like water with thirty spoons of table salt mixed in it. I had to muster up all my will power to gulp down that one sip. I looked around to see if anyone noticed my expression but everyone was busy sipping their own salt water.

I took my glass and turned away to the door of the barn. I took another sip and it was torture. If only I could walk out and empty some in the bushes, the devil in me whispered. I will cheat the system if I have the opportunity. I had cheated with respect to so many things—exams, pocket money, disowning blame; I cheated whenever I could if I knew I would not be find out. As a result, my studies had no value for me, I spent money frivolously, and I didn't have any real friends or relationships. When I cheated another person, I actually cheated myself. I cheated myself into living the life of a thief, never benefitting from my loot, be it education, money or relationships.

Just a few sips down and three-fourths of the glass still remained. My head spun and my stomach churned. The whispers in my head grew louder: "Cheat. Throw it. Walk out carefully and very cleverly empty it in the bushes. Leave the last few sips, walk back and drink the end. Simple. No one will know." Except my own spirit that would be denied the opportunity of waking up to its purpose.

I stood there, my hands trembling, breaking into a cold

sweat. "I can't do this," my whole body screamed. And then, with one final go, I lifted the glass and gulped down all its contents. Like a person who bottoms up on a tequila shot, I staggered and sat down on the chair. I burped an embarrassingly loud burp; my system had accepted the salt. Everyone turned around and looked in my direction; they were still going on with their drink.

"Now what?" I asked myself.

"Five glasses of the salt water in the day. Nothing else. Only this. Anytime, whenever. You have till afternoon," Kahuna said, walking out of the barn as though the stench of my burp was unbearable.

I put my hand to my mouth and exhaled—there was no smell. I sat in silence, paying attention to the roller coaster ride that had started in my belly.

Four more glasses to go. I could not stomach the thought of gulping down four more glasses. My feet felt grounded, my spine lifted my body and I turned and walked towards the table, determined to deal with the salt. I reached out for the jug and filled another glass of salt water as everyone eyed me with amusement. I walked back to my chair, cupped my hands around the glass, and closed my eyes.

I had to do this. There was no escape. There was no option. Responsibility is a salt drink. You may hate getting up every morning and going to work but a man's got to do what a man's got to do. A woman in labour may wish for a painless delivery but such is the price of life, such is the price of living.

I raised the glass to my lips but before I could take a sip I felt a shooting pain in my stomach. It was as though I had been stabbed with a sharp knife. The glass almost fell out of my hand and I sat down on the floor. Placing the glass on the ground, I held my stomach. I was in extreme pain. Another shooting pain and I knew I had to run to the toilet. I found the strength to get up. Still holding my stomach tight, I staggered out towards the cubicle Kahuna had indicated.

It was a hay thatched cubicle, about six square feet in size. I saw a metal container with a sling handle, like a paint can, outside the cubicle. I picked it up with one hand, the other not letting go of my stomach. I entered the cubicle; there was nothing inside, no commode, no chair, no nothing, except some toilet paper rolls in the corner. You didn't need a commode or WC if you had to poop in a container after all. This was no time to throw a tantrum or go storming to Kahuna. I was under pressure. And when one is under pressure of any sort, there is no argument, only release. I sat down and released my welling pain in a small container with an embarrassingly loud explosion.

In one mighty shot I had filled up half the container. I was so embarrassed at what I was doing that I did not even want to accept that this was me. I was in a tiny cubicle with nothing but a metal container under my butt and creating a musical orchestra with the plain wind in my stomach. I absolutely refused to accept this reality and mentally packed off this moment and threw it as far away as I could. I would never acknowledge this, I thought.

I got out of the cubicle. Sain was waiting outside. I didn't know which way to look. I wished the ground would split open and I could bury myself. I was so embarrassed. Sain pushed me out of the way. He had no time for my embarrassment; he was a man on a mission.

I guess we all worry about what others think of us and we hide away from our own shortcomings. We beat ourselves down on issues which in fact are of no interest to others. In a few seconds a volcano erupted in the cubicle. I was relieved. I was not alone.

In reality we are not alone. We think we are the chosen ones, the special ugly ducklings, but everyone shares the same fate, only we don't know that about each other. Sometimes we are so embarrassed with our fallacies that we hide behind the curtain of fake sophistication and lose out on the compassion that we can share and receive from each other. If we have no tolerance for our own shortcomings how can we be tolerant of others? Imagine a whole species living in a trap, walled out from each other's love. That is how we live, estranged from each other, without love or understanding. We forget that we are one.

The shamans have a very beautiful greeting when they meet a stranger: "In Lak'ech" (I am another you). How beautiful, I am another you. How naive to think that I am different or I am the only one. We are all the same beings, the same force, partaking of the same pressure and the same passion.

I walked towards the barn. There was no one inside. Everyone was in the barn cubicles, cleansing the toxic waste from their bodies. My dizziness and pain had disappeared; I felt light. Another glass of salt water didn't seem all that bad. It was difficult at the start but by now my body had accepted the initial shock and the following consequence. The human body is an amazing machine. It adapts and accommodates very fast. That is how habits are formed.

I went through four glasses of salt water with some difficulty and spent the entire morning and afternoon alternately filling glasses and metal containers! By late afternoon the last glass of salt water had long been consumed but the trips to the cubicle continued. The intervals between each trip increased until my stomach was stable and there was no longer anything left inside except clean, flushed interiors. Wow. I felt squeaky clean and wished I could take a peek inside to see the new me.

"You can wait if you want to," Emma said. "I am done." She

walked away without waiting for my answer. I decided to wait.

"I'm done too," Sain added. "Leave your containers piled in the spot assigned to you," he informed while leaving the barn.

I was alone. The others had already left without any acknowledgment or instruction. I was content. It had been an easy test, not such a great challenge. Yes, the first glass had been torture, as had been the first trip to the cubicle, but after that I had been fine. I wondered why Kahuna had made such a big deal about it.

"Many people fail the test," he had said, but we all had passed with flying colours, or had we? I frowned. There had to be a catch somewhere, I was convinced.

I got up and walked away to the cottage. I needed a bath. A serious scrub bath. I entered the room and realised I was bather number four in the queue. Later, after a long refreshing bath, we came down to the kitchen. There were more jugs of water lined up. "This is spring water," Kahuna said, "to replenish the minerals and essential vitamins that you have flushed out. Drink as much as you like. At sunset we will conclude the ritual. It would be nice if you can get some sleep; your body needs to recharge."

I was the first to grab the jug. I was eager to taste the spring water. It was refreshing but I could not have more than one glass. One thing the salt cleanse had certainly done was that it had cleansed away greed. My body would accept only what it needed and not what my mind wanted to stuff. I drank the glass of water and headed for my room. Drowsiness had suddenly overtaken me and I needed to sleep.

Before anyone else could get into the room, I had already slipped into bed. The words "spiritual challenge" floated before my eyes as I fell into a deep, dreamless sleep.

When I woke up in the afternoon the sun was lazily dipping towards the horizon. There was an orchestra of snores, Emma's being the loudest. I had always thought it so un-womanly but now I had no comment. She must have been very tired or just relishing her sleep; Emma's snores didn't bother me. I wore my tracks, picked up my coat, and went down into the garden to catch the last warmth of the sun before the cold set in.

I saw Kahuna walking with a few other medicine. men carrying stacks of wood on their shoulders. They were headed towards a small clearing in the distance, about three hundred feet from the cottage, piling up the wood there. Maybe there would be a fire walk at night, I thought. But the word "spiritual challenge" still seemed to be stuck in my head.

Mary came out with another jug of spring water. "Don't drink too much," she warned, "the ritual will just about start and you don't want your bladder taking your attention away from the process." I nodded thankfully. That was a good tip. I was really thirsty but sipped on the water as though it was a nice expensive wine, experiencing every molecule of it.

In a few minutes Emma was down. It was a quick transition from snores to strides. She looked fresh as the morning dew. "You look so fresh," she exclaimed. "You too," I responded. It was the result of the cleansing process and I was happy with the compliment.

The sound of drums filled the air. Soft drums, like the ones marking the start of a tribal ritual. I was electrified. Next, I saw a fire light up in the distance.

"We are starting the ritual," Emma said, putting down her glass of water. She took my arm and we started in the direction of the beating drums and the dancing flames. "Spiritual challenge," I said to myself. I was willing to explore.

There were small rugs placed around the fire to seat five people. A white cloth lay neatly wrapped on each rug. "You will wear this robe for the ritual," a medicine man said, pointing to the white cloth. Kahuna was in a trance, beating the drums.

I looked around for a place to change. The others just took off their clothes and slipped into their robes. The medicine man too did the same. I slipped on the robe over my head and struggled to remove my shirt and tracks from under it. I had not yet blended into the "I'm cool about taking off my clothes in public" mentality. It took a few minutes for my head to emerge out of the robe. I had lost the ability to change clothes in weird places since leaving college. Changing in a car to jam with friends was a distant but pleasant memory. I had clearly lost my touch. The drums got louder and my attention was now focussed on the dancing flames and on Kahuna who was obviously in a trance.

Very soon I got engrossed in the drum beats. It was the kind of music that grows on you and takes over. Just when I found myself swaying to the rhythm it stopped abruptly. There was silence except for the crackle of the wood amidst the dancing flames.

The drummers left their drums and went away. Kahuna was still lost in his trance. As I watched him fixedly, he slowly opened his eyes and looked straight at me. His gaze was soft and he soon turned his eyes towards the fire. In the distance I could see the drummers returning in a line with a long stick on their shoulders. On the stick were hung all the containers that we had left at the hay thatch cubicles.

They approached the fire and began to place the containers in a circle around it. Cooking the contents was not something

I had expected. I couldn't figure out what Kahuna had in mind. The drummers finished lining the fire pit with the containers and stood next to the drums.

Kahuna stood up, a meter away from the circle, facing us.

"You will now be engaged in a ritual that will challenge your spirit to sit up and take notice of its existence. These containers contain your excreta, whatever that means to you. Ronnie," he said, pointing to a drummer who was standing beside him, "will take one container and empty it in your palms and you will accept and acknowledge the contents of the container. I want you to feel and experience the contents and when you have fully acknowledged what your hands hold, release it with a touch of your forehead into the fire." Kahuna turned away and sat between the two drummers who had now started to beat a very gentle rhythm.

"What!!" my whole being screamed so loud that the entire universe must have heard my exclamation of horror. He was going to pour a container full of shit in my palms and I had to accept it. Helloo!! Wait a minute. I didn't even know whether that was my shit. It could be anyone's shit. I was supposed to hold it in my hands, acknowledge it and touch it to my forehead. Was he mad? What kind of gross ritual was this! I was getting out of there.

When Sain stood up and walked away I almost did the same. I turned my head and saw him striding towards the cottage. He did not slow down or turn back. Within seconds Emma too got up, stared at the fire, and said an apologetic prayer. Even before she finished making the sign of the cross, Rick got up. He walked away first and Emma followed.

What was going on? I went through a range of emotions from confusion to disgust. It was too much for me to handle. My mind was in a whirl and my brain felt messed up.

I looked at the fire. I looked at Kahuna. Why was I doing this? I wanted to walk out. I was not taking someone else's shit in my hand and acknowledging it. No way. The more I protested the more firm my body became. The more I wanted to run, the more my legs locked in. I felt trapped between a mind wanting to run away and a mind wanting to persist.

"Would you like to leave too?" Kahuna asked.

"No," a voice emerged from my mouth but I could swear I didn't say it.

"Are you crazy? Don't believe this voice. That's not me. I want to say yes, but something is making me say no. This is a conspiracy," I screamed in my head. But my wanting-to-persist mind finally won.

I surrendered. It was a meaningless fight.

"We will start the ritual. Your task is to observe and acknowledge the excreta that will be poured in your palms. All containers will be presented for your acknowledgement. Once you have acknowledged the contents in your palm, offer them as prayer in the fire. You can leave the ritual at any point. How far you will go depends on how far you want to go. Your journey is your choice." Kahuna motioned to the drummer who now bent over and opened the lid of a container on his side and carried it towards me.

As if by instinct my hands folded into a cup right above my lap. The white robe covered the top of my thighs; my legs were bare thighs down. As the man approached me my eyes fixed on my palms. The stench of human faeces filled the air. It was the stench you don't want to own up to when your stomach releases toxic leftovers of the junk food you happily consumed without a second thought. It entered my nostrils and stung my brains.

Before I could think any further, I felt soft human shit being poured in my palms. My small hands filled in a jiffy and the rest of it tricked off my hands onto my robe and my legs. My hands trembled as I held the human shit in my hands. I looked at it. It was of a colour you never want to have in your wardrobe and it felt creepier than the creepiest insects from Fear Factor. I sat still.

I continued to observe the thick mass in my hands. I was covered with excreta. I began to think analytically. Was this filthy shit or was it just finely processed digested food? I could, in that instant, see the whole process that takes place in the human body to sustain life. We eat food to survive; if we don't we will eventually die. What people don't consider is that we will also die if we do not excrete out the food that we have eaten. If there is no intake for a long period, the human body will perish. So too, if there is no output for a long period. What sustains life is the movement, the flow. The shit was the outflow of what was accepted into the body.

The smell of the human waste was not pleasant but it was real. There was no escape from the reality. When one eats food, the stomach and the intestines very cleverly extract all that is required to sustain life for the organism. They have about four to five hours to do their work. As the food passes through the stomach into the intestines on its way out, it is processed, inspected and broken down into digestible form. The solid apple is broken down into small molecules which are absorbed in the blood to sustain life. The balance is thrown out to make space for the new cycle.

So how can food be good and shit be bad? Why must food be served with glamour and glory, and shit be shunned with embarrassment and apology? Both are essential processes.

Either I was possessed or something had been ignited in my soul because I felt a newfound respect for the human

waste that now dripped continuously from my hand onto
my calves. As if in a trance my hands reached my forehead
and I stretched to pour the remains into the fire. Promptly
the drummer carried another can and began to pour it
with great respect in my hands. He poured it with the same
dedication that a priest reserves for the holy water he pours
in your palms during prayer.

I didn't know whose container was being emptied into my
hands. It didn't matter. One lot of shit is no better or worse
than another. Shit is shit. Any kind of shit; even the "shit"
we dump on others in our daily interactions. So many times
someone else has paid the price for my doing. In other
words, someone else has got my shit. So many times we pass
our crap around and someone who doesn't deserve it gets
to be in the firing line. When people fail to own up and take
responsibility for their shit, someone else gets it. In this
case, I literally got other people's shit.

As the new crap poured into my hands and dripped onto my
robes I treated it with greater acceptance than the last lot.
This is a cycle, I told myself. Food and shit are important
and are two sides of the same coin, like birth and death, or
happiness and grief. Nothing is good or bad. Everything is
important for the cycle and the sustenance of life. To rejoice
in one and shun the other signifies denying oneself the
experience of the fullness of life. I was in a state of neutral
existence. There was no dirt or filth. It was only matter.

The drummer kept pouring the shit in my hands and I
acknowledged and prayed. I did not count the containers
and it didn't matter how much shit was loaded on me.
I acknowledged and prayed and I let it go. I could not
differentiate between my waste and another's. It was the
same. I could not tell the difference. And if I couldn't tell
which one was mine then I was in every container.

As I released the last bit of shit in the fire I cupped my

palms again for more but it was over. I was covered in shit from head to toe. I became the shit. And I was ok. It was a process.

By now I had lost all judgement of good or bad. Suddenly there was nothing that was bad because even what I thought was bad was necessary for the cycle of life. It was necessary to live. It was necessary to enjoy life. So what is really bad? Without shit, food has no role. Food, if does not become shit, will become poison and kill the body. If there is no shit. to balance out all that we consider good then we will create a self-destructing mechanism.

"Please get up," the drummer almost whispered in my ear. I sprang to my feet not bothered at all by the disgusting sight I presented. There was a huge tub to my right and the drummer beckoned me to step into it. As the drums began to beat louder with more vigorous beats, a bucketful of water came gushing down my head, and I could feel layers of human faeces wash away. Another bucketful and yet another followed as I shivered and dripped in the cold.

Kahuna walked up to me and began to smudge hot ash on my face and head. He then began to scrub me with the hot ash as he dashed between the fire pit and me. The smell of the excreta was vanishing and I was covered in ash like a statue being sculpted.

The ash felt warm and I could feel a layer freezing on my body. Kahuna began to whisk the essence of sage leaves in my direction until my lungs were filled with the essence. He then smudged the sage ashes on my head and I could feel an electric ray run from my head down to my toes. With my feet still in the tub, five bucketfuls of water were poured gently on me until I was free from all the ash and my flesh was clean.

The drummer gently lifted me off my feet. He placed me on

the ground 180 ° from the place where I was sitting so I was now on the opposite side. Two men picked up the tub of water I had been washed in and with one haul poured it on the fire. The flames died out with a loud hiss.

The night was young, the stars gleaming in the spotless sky. Kahuna patted my head and sat down opposite me. The smoke was still settling down from the wet embers fighting to stay alive.

"Accepting waste with no judgement is respecting life to its fullest. You cannot respect one end of the process and loathe the other. You will never live life till you accept death. You will never truly experience success till you make peace with failure. The spirit that is neutral about both processes and treats them with the same passion and respect is a spirit that is cleansed of its need to judge, to compare, and worst of all, to classify. In your partaking of the process you have released yourself of judgement of good or bad and right or wrong because in reality they do not exist. The only thing that is real is your acceptance or your denial. When you accept, you understand; when you deny, you create a toxic experience. A spirit that judges can never be in alignment with its purpose because judgement is the enemy of purpose. In your acceptance of the ritual you understand that I am another you."

I understood more than I could explain. In releasing the waste in the fire, I had let go of all blame, all judgement, all grudges, and all bitterness. I had observed, acknowledged, and released it all in prayer. My spirit was cleansed.

"It is spring water tonight. Your body deserves the purity that your soul feels," Kahuna said, pulling me in an embrace. "You have passed the test," he said, gently touching my feet. "It is an honour to know you."

He took my hand and silently led me into the cottage. It was dark and empty. The others had gone off to sleep, I guessed. I entered the room and was surprised to find everyone awake. Rick was the first to get up and embrace me heartily without saying a word. Sain followed and so did Emma. They didn't let go for a long time. I felt tears rolling down my cheeks and we all broke into sobs. Sobs that said, "I'm sorry for all the judgement and pretence." Sobs that said, "I accept you, the way you are!"

"Why did you leave the ritual?" I asked Emma, still sobbing as she offered me a glass of the spring water.

"It is a part of the ritual," Emma said, now kneeling down on the floor beside me. "That was to lead you out, to tempt you to leave. So often we join in the judgement, in the gossip, and in the ridicule by our mere presence or absence. We know what is right and what is wrong but somehow what becomes real is mass mentality. We don't want to be left alone, especially if it is to face shit. So everyone runs. We ran away and left the door open for you to follow. That was the first challenge you had to overcome, to stay alone with all the shit. And you did."

"Many fail right there," Rick added. "It takes a very determined spirit in ruthless pursuit of its own liberation to have the courage to follow its own purpose rather than someone else's escape."

Sain placed his hand on my head and I sobbed some more.

I don't know why I cried myself to sleep that night. It was as though I was letting go of some crap I had held on to for long. Whose crap? Mine or someone else's? I could not tell and it did not matter. It flowed out as salty tears from my body, and I was cleansed.

My experiences 'lessoned' for you:

•••> Challenges are important to life. Without challenges you cannot grow or have the opportunity to re-discover yourself.

•••> You will never know everything. Knowledge unfolds as we move forward. Sitting back and waiting to know everything before we do anything is a waste of life.

•••> When things get tough, lie low if you must. Giving in to allow the storm to pass is not the same as giving up.

•••> Being "willing" is more important than being "ready". Ready is not the first step, willing is.

•••> You never cheat anyone else, you only cheat yourself. The price of cheating is that you never benefit. In fact you reduce that very thing from your experience.

•••> Responsibility is like a salt water drink. It's difficult to gulp but defines your character and cleanses your soul.

•••> Pressure is a signal for action, for movement, for release.

•••> In tolerating your own shortcomings you subconsciously give permission to others to do the same. By being tolerant of your own fallacies you become tolerant of others.

•••> I am another you. I am no different. If I can be, then you can too.

•••> Happiness and sorrow are two sides of the same coin. Both are necessary to complete the cycle. You don't rejoice in one and shun another. You treat both, with equal respect and grace.

•••> Judgement is the enemy of purpose. When you judge and classify your actions and those of others you lose sight of your own purpose.

•••> To escape is mass mentality, but to stand your ground and to follow your purpose takes character and courage that leads you to your own liberation.

The Drummer's Edge

· ·

I woke up in the morning with a sore head. Lack of sleep, I thought. I looked around and found all the other beds empty. I was always the last to get up. I loved to sleep, especially after a weary night. The alarm on my cell phone had got into snooze mode half a dozen times, until I gave up and got up. I cannot wake up without an alarm. Sometimes I think if I were allowed the liberty to sleep on, I would never wake up. "Age is catching up with you," my brother always joked and sometimes I frightened myself by believing him.

It is the many years of work, real hard work, that has taken a toll on my health. I have always lived life on the edge with high energy, 400 volt enthusiasm, walking the thin line between madness and passion. Life has always been a celebration; no matter what work I did, I did it queen-size. But now, tapping that energy is sometimes a struggle and I have started disliking waking up early.

The only advantage of waking up late was that I got to take my own time in the bathroom without fear of intrusion or delay. The salt cleanse had made my stomach queasy and unsettled. It was a relief knowing the bathroom had no "hurry up" pressure from the outside.

Today I was getting ready to meet Ruud. He was the keeper of a ritual called the Drummer's Edge, which he was coming over to the farm to initiate. I had heard so much about him that I had already begun to like him. I had this image of a Red Indian native type of man, maybe with the rough looks of a medicine man. I was eager to take part in his Drummer's ritual.

"It is only for men," Emma had said. I had vehemently protested until it was settled that Ruud would decide. I had to get Ruud to say yes.

I brushed my teeth and showered. I even took the time to blow dry my hair. I wanted to look and feel my very best. Getting ready is my personal feel-good ritual. I spend a good two hours on myself in the morning. I love it. I look at myself, admire myself, and even smile at myself in the mirror. On the border of my mirror I have written out messages telling myself that I am a star, I am loved, I am super rich, I am pretty, I am young, I am energetic, I am passionate, I am love. These decorate the borders of my mirror. And I absolutely love what I see. I walk the thin line between vanity and self love, and I must say I love myself. Today, I spent time in love with me.

I came down for breakfast and all that was left was some wheat bread and of course coffee. I am not a fussy person. I knew the consequences of being late. I knew I would miss breakfast and I was ready for leftovers. I picked up my cup of coffee and some bread, whisked an apple from the tray, and headed outside.

It was cold but I was wearing Mary's fur coat. As I sipped my coffee, Mary came up from the back. "Didn't you go to meet Ruud?" she asked.

"He is here?" I was startled and almost gulped some hot coffee, burning my tongue.

"Yes, he arrived this morning. Everyone went to meet him," Mary said, gathering the leftover cups from the garden table and heading inside.

Now this is what happens while I sleep. The world passes me by. I wanted to meet Ruud. I wanted to make a good impression. I wanted to be part of his ritual. I had even told Emma that I would be there to receive him. And now I was unable to keep my commitment. I was already losing points with Ruud and I was certain Emma would make some comment about my sleep and how I was terrible at waking up.

"First round lost," I thought. "Plan your next move." I sat munching on the apple and saw the clouds floating by. Spotless white, like specks of cotton dispersed in the sky. I saw the eagles, effortlessly flying and enjoying their flight. I had seen many birds perched on the trees or hopping around but the eagle was best seen in flight. It obviously loved to fly and that must be the secret behind its effortless movement. If I had a chance to converse with the eagle and ask why it flew all day I'm sure it would say, "Because I love the sky." Love. That has been the driving force of my life and I have spent thirty years in love with all I do.

"Daydreaming?" I heard Rick's voice as he jumped over the fence and landed near the garden table. I just smiled. I had no urge to explain or defend. I was in love. It was the group of people emerging behind Rick that made me stand up.

"Ruud is here," Rick said. I saw five men walking alongside Emma. Which one was Ruud? My mind raced. All of them looked like ordinary villagers, dressed in loose khaki pants and loose shirts. All wore earth coloured attire and had long hair.

"I'm Ruud," one of the men said as he stretched out his hand. He was about 6 feet 3 inches tall, well built, his long blond hair tied in a ponytail and wearing rectangular spectacles. My hand was lost in his as I mumbled a faint hello.

"Pleased to meet you. I have heard so much about you ever

since I arrived. I was eager to meet you," Ruud said with the warmest smile I have ever seen. Now that was *my* line. He stole my words and now I was speechless. I guess when you think too much and plan too much and rehearse too much, you are stumped if the equation is changed. But if you just allow yourself to go with the experience you discover new heights to a relationship.

"Let me get you guys some coffee and breakfast," Emma said, entering the cottage.

Before I could regain my composure enough to speak, the four men had walked away with Rick.

"So what brings you here?" Ruud asked, looking deep into my eyes. His sharp gaze pierced my eyes and touched my soul.

"I don't know," I said. And that usually is my answer to everything at first. "I don't know."

"What if you knew why you were here? What would that be?" Ruud asked, now gazing deeper into my eyes.

"Well, I am here because I want to grow. I want to know who I am and why I am here on this planet," I said, and I was startled at my own confession. That was so crisp and precise. Even though I had not thought of this before, I was able to answer without "thinking". I was answering out of "knowing". And there is a vast difference between the two. The difference is between what you know and what you think you know. And what you know is always far more than you ever thought you did.

"That's great. At some point or the other, we all embark on that journey. Some fall off midway when they can't face the challenge of confronting themselves while others persist ruthlessly and move beyond themselves. They discover the spirit that lay dormant under the guise of a perishable body. It's admirable that you travelled this far in your quest. You are a woman of extreme persistence. You are one of those rare people who get what they want." Ruud spoke with a deep knowing. He spoke as though he knew me.

I was silent. I didn't know what to say. The half-eaten apple had oxidised in my hand and I could see a crow eyeing it relentlessly. I threw the apple in the direction of the crow and he caught it before it hit the ground. The crow got what it wanted. If you persist, you win. Although the crow got the apple it did not mean that I had to go hungry. I had soul food with Ruud; the apple was no longer needed. In the bargain of give and take, give does not make you less and take does not make you more. It is just a shift in possession and a shift in perception.

"Why do you want to do the drumming?" Ruud got straight to the point. He reached inside his pocket and pulled out a single cigarette.

"I don't know. . ." I started and almost laughed aloud. "But if I knew why I wanted to do the drumming, it is because I want to experience a process that will free my soul. I want to find liberation. Somewhere deep inside I feel trapped. I feel that I am not free. I feel that I am weighed down and I am not doing what I really want to do. Somewhere I feel that there is more to me and that I will never know myself because my soul is trapped. I don't know what the trap is but I feel it when I shirk what I should do. I feel it when I don't stand up for myself. I feel it when I allow myself to be blamed for things I did not mess up. I feel it most when I am convinced that I am not worthy of greatness. I want to break free. I cannot bear to live in this trap. Help me. I will do whatever it takes. I will go all the way." I paused for breath.

"Do you think you can allow me to be a part of the drumming?" I almost pleaded.

"Who am I to allow or disallow? It is your will. I am just the keeper of the process," Ruud shrugged.

That was easy, I thought. Emma had made it sound so difficult. She had said that women could not take part in the drumming and that it was a process for men only. I did not bother to bring it up lest it sounded like I was complaining about Emma. I kept quiet and was happy that I was accepted without a fight. All the mental conversations that I had rehearsed suddenly went to waste.

I guess that is what happens when we choose to see our reality through someone else's eyes. It is never the same. When people explain their perception of reality to us it colours our own assessment of situations. The only person who knows and can ever build your reality is you. I thought of every instance when I was warned by friends about people, about things, about relationships, about places. I realised that most of the time my experience was different. When people give their advice or opinions what they are actually doing is expressing the nature of their own relationship with that person or situation. Your relationship and your actions are best directed by you. To act in accordance with other people's opinions will only create the same relationship as theirs. The best way to decide about a relationship is to act objectively and independently.

"Shall we do the drumming tomorrow? "Ruud asked. "We have much to prepare today."

Emma emerged with a tray of fresh smelling coffee and some mushrooms on toast. I was ready for a feast.

"You get what you want, don't you?" Emma smiled.

I smiled back. I was happy. Sometimes there is no need for words and sometimes the best way to express yourself is by saying nothing at all.

We ate and we chatted. Ruud had walked all the way from Belgium for six days. He believed in the journey more than in the destination. He believed that technology and speed in everything stole the joy of the journey. Growth is in the journey, never in the destination. He believed that he travelled here to allow spiritual growth and that he had his share of learning on the way. This way he would share more, because he was more.

Unknowingly I have enjoyed my journeys. Even in the flights I write or I read. I am never asleep. If I am getting somewhere, I am happy. I am a window seat person, whatever the mode of travel. My head is at the window like an excited puppy. I am alive. I am observant and ticking when I travel. I feel I grow with every journey. I think better, I feel better. Even till date, when I am not feeling too bright, I get into my car and go for a drive, and when I return I have found my enthusiastic self.

"Are you ready for the process?" Ruud inquired. "Or do you want to sleep?" he chuckled.

Emma roared with laughter. "Her waking up is a ritual," she jokingly told Ruud. "The alarm must ring six times before she opens her eyes." I gave her a dirty look and jumped out of my chair threatening to chase her. She scurried into the cottage, still laughing.

"Yes, I am ready and I am awake," I smiled at Ruud.

"Then let's go," he said standing up.

Ruud and I walked across the farm into the fields. I almost had to jog to keep pace with him. The speed of my 5 feet 2 inches frame was no comparison to his. In the distance I could see a road—we were approaching the highway.

"To be a part of the drumming ritual, you first have to make your drum," Ruud said.

"Oh," was all I had to say. "How must I do that?"

"You will see," Ruud said, his eyes searching for something in the distance. "There they are!" he said, pointing to a group of men by the highway.

We were a few meters from the highway and I saw Rick and the four men standing there at the edge of the road. There were little carts parked by the side of a tree, with a few spades and some rucksacks.

Rick was smiling as we approached him. His smile said, "You get what you want, don't you?" I didn't know that my being allowed in the drumming process was such a big breakthrough.

Ruud spoke with the other four men in Dutch and they nodded. Ruud turned around and beckoned to me to sit with him. The highway was a lazy road—a car buzzed by every five to seven minutes. The quiet was in sharp contrast to the madness found in the streets of New York or Mumbai. I sat facing Ruud under a beautiful birch tree.

"You have to find your animal to make the drum," Ruud said. My heart sank. My stomach began to churn and a sort of nausea built up. The body reacts so fast to words and the meanings we attach to them.

"I have to hunt?" my soul was shrieking aloud in my body. No wonder Emma said it was man's ritual. I have been a vegetarian all my life. I love animals alive and not on my plate. I am a volunteer in several foundations that protect and serve animals. I look after stray and abandoned creatures. I feel that we have stolen the homes of animals in our attempt at urbanisation and the least I can do is help a helpless dog or cat or crow, whatever. And here I was, partaking in a ritual to free my soul by killing an animal to make a drum!

I wanted to run away and never come back. I had made a mistake. I had wanted the wrong thing. I had wanted wrong things many times without even knowing what the consequences would be. I had protested and fought and desired that thing only to achieve it and realise that it was not what I wanted. The achievement felt as useless as the effort and the journey.

I sat under the tree, pale and frozen.

"Are you ok? "Ruud asked.

"I don't know," I croaked.

"So you have to find your animal to make the drum. Jacques will accompany you along the highway with the wheel barrow and you will pick up a dead animal that has been killed on the road."

"Huh?" I could hear my heart beating again. "A dead animal on the road?" I asked with more energy in my voice.

"We do not kill animals to use their skin for our ritual. However we use the spiritual karma of an animal killed in impact or accident on the road. See, here is how it goes. Death must be natural to the living. Which means every living being should be allowed the opportunity to know death. This happens just before a living being dies. When an eagle chases a rat across the field, in that chase the rat knows death. The rat knows death even before the eagle can touch it. And the blow with the claws of the eagle releases the spirit of the rat and it moves on. But when a rat is crossing the road and is killed in an impact, it is not allowed to know death and so its spirit is not released. You will find a dead animal on the road and Jacques will help you with a space cleansing ritual. The ritual frees the space of the energy of confusion and allows a clear passage for the travellers to follow. You will load the body of the animal in the cart and bring it back for processing, where we will allow its spirit to be released and use it remains for spiritual prayer processes," Ruud explained.

I remembered the "talking stick" from the sweat lodge and understood what Ruud meant by using the remains of dead animals in spiritual prayers.

I stood up along with Ruud. I was amazed and still a little dizzy with all the emotional rush of a sheer misunderstanding. I could think of so many times when I drew my own conclusions in conversations without really understanding the other person's point of view. And I could think of so many times when I formed my judgements about people in just a few words without even allowing them to express themselves fully. If I had acted out of my own limitations and reactions today I would have lost out on a process to liberate my soul.

Before I knew it Jacques was standing in front of me, smiling. I could see I was the first woman he had seen participate in the drumming process. "You are very blessed," he said. That was the greatest first meeting comment I have ever heard. And since he said it, I believed it. So many times we believe people when they comment about us without inspecting the solidity of their opinion. Even if we don't believe them, we still get affected by their comments. When people tell us that we have put on weight or that we are looking tired we believe them. Sometimes I think humans are the stupidest species on planet earth; they believe without inspection and act without reason. I once told my dog, "You look tired." And she jumped right up and licked my nose. My opinion did not decide her state of being but others' opinions sure shape ours.

I was on top of the world. I was qualified as a person who

got what she wanted and I was blessed. That was an amazing start to a brand new life. My soul was listening.

Jacques and I started off on the highway with a wheel barrow, a spade, and a small bundle of wood shavings. The smell of sage leaves was familiar and I could see a box of matches in Jacques' shirt pocket. Jacques pulled my arm towards him as a car whizzed by. "You don't want to be in the wheel barrow," he chuckled.

"So, we are looking for a dead animal to make a drum. It is an incredible act of kindness to release the souls of the poor stuck beings," Jacques spoke with compassion.

Rick and the others were also trudging along with a wheel barrow ahead of us on the other side of the road. They would also be a part of the drumming, I assumed.

"Do many animals die on the road?" I asked Jacques, trying to make conversation. "I don't know," he said, looking into the distance.

"Are you a medicine man?" I continued my chat.

"No," he laughed. "I work in a motel in Belgium. I came along with Ruud. I always like to be a part of his processes. And this time he said I could serve. So I took the opportunity and came here. And as my luck would have it, I am serving you." He smiled, looking at me warmly, as though it was an honour to be with me.

"When you experience liberation you are compelled to help in the liberation of others," he continued.

"I found a fox," a voice ahead shouted out. It was Rick. The other four men and Ruud had gathered there. It was a beautiful fox, not dead for long. The men lifted up its limp body by the legs. There was no blood. It had died of shock, it seemed. I had not seen a dead animal so close. I was choked. It was beautiful. It was killed in someone's journey; two paths had crossed at the wrong junction, at the wrong time.

"You can continue," Ruud waved at us. I wanted to wait and watch what would happen next. I supposed when my turn came, I would.

"I found a beaver," someone ahead of us shouted.

"I found a fox," another voice announced.

I wondered what I would find. I walked on, suddenly solemn. The fox was still beautiful. It was dead but it was beautiful. I could not shake that image off my mind.

As we walked, Jacques pushing the wheel barrow, I spotted something in the distance. The others seemed to have passed it by. "Look," I said to Jacques pointing towards a bush ahead, "there is a dead animal." Jacques did not acknowledge my find. As we walked, I edged towards the bush, not noticing that Jacques was not following. I went to the bush and saw a dead wild cat. It had been dead a long time, black blood around its chest, and a dried open wound. Its eyes were open and so was its mouth. Its body was stiff and it looked scary.

"Look," I said to Jacques and he noticed the worry on my face. "It's a wild cat."

"Well, you found it," Jacques said, "let's take it." And he rolled the wheel barrow over.

I must admit that I was not very excited about my find. The others had found foxes and beavers. I was also looking for an interesting animal but what I found instead was a cat. I had seen cats before. I had never seen a fox or a beaver. I did not want the cat. I wanted something more exotic. But the cat it was.

Jacques bent down near the cat and opened the little pouch of wooden shavings. He dished out a coral shell and placed it on the ground. Then, crushing some sage leaves together, he lit a match. As the sage leaves began to smoke, he waved the fumes towards the body of the cat with his hand while chanting a hymn. I did not know whether to sit down or remain standing, so I stood by, trying not to look at the face of the dead cat.

After chanting for about two minutes, Jacques scooped up the dead creature in the shovel. He placed it ever so gently in the wheel barrow and covered it with a gunny bag. He knelt down again and dusted the place with the ashes of the sage leaves, and waved the fumes of the remaining simmering leaves on the ground where the cat lay a few minutes before.

Without a word, he turned the wheel barrow around and I followed suit.

By this time I began to sense that something was not right. There was a very different energy about Jacques. "Is something the matter?" I asked.

"We usually do not make drums out of cat skin," Jacques replied.

"Oh!" I exclaimed. So would I be disqualified now? Would I not be allowed in the ritual? Was it over? Was finding a cat a bad omen? Why was I always the one to pick the wrong choices? What was wrong with me?

A single statement from Jacques had made my mind race in different directions. That is how I have always been. When I am labelled "different", which I always am, my first response is to assume it must connote something negative, that I must be bad and that something must be wrong with me. I can beat myself down six feet under if someone rejects me or makes an unfriendly remark about my work.

"So what does that mean?" I gathered some courage to ask, silently preparing myself for a devastating answer.

"I don't know," Jacques answered genuinely. "Ruud will explain."

I did not want to face Ruud anymore. Everyone was returning with some nice animal and I had found a long dead and decomposed cat. I now understood why the others had passed the cat by: they did not make drums with dead cats. But someone should have told me what to look for, or more importantly, what not to look for. My fear of being the unlucky one turned into anger towards those who had not bothered to guide me.

Through every unhappy or painful event of my life I have felt the need to know who the cause of my discomfort was. That is how I have made peace with all that was wrong in my life. If the fault was mine, it brought shame and fear; if someone else was to blame, it angered me. I have journeyed between shame and fear and anger for most of my life. No matter which one was dominant, I was always miserable.

We reached the place where we had met at the start of our quest. The others were already there and I could see the smoke from Ruud's cigarette. He started to walk towards us and I wanted to sink into the ground with every step.

As we met, Ruud smiled and gave me a hug. "Let's go," he said, still holding on to my shoulders.

We walked back to the farm. I did not bring up the cat nor did he ask what I had found. It was a journey in silence and

I was beginning to feel sick.

The sun was up marking noon and the weather was pleasant. I took off my coat and put it on the chair outside the cottage.

Jacques and Rick had lined up all the wheel barrows alongside the tree nearby. We washed our hands and feet in the water from the hand pump near the barn. Everyone was silent, merely acknowledging each other's presence with a smile.

Once back in the garden, I sat at the table, staring into the distance. Ruud came and sat beside me, smelling of smoke. "We will start the skinning in some time," he said. "You need not do it. Jacques will do it for you."

I was happy that I did not have to do it. I did not know whether to tell Ruud that I had found a cat or just let him find out. It was the same feeling I used to have as a child, when I had messed up and my mom would wait for my dad to come home so I could be punished. When my dad walked into the house, I never knew which would be easier—to confess to my prank or allow my mom to tell her story. It always landed up as mom's story and that always got me in trouble with my father.

I decided to take my chances today. "I found a dead wild cat," I blurted out. "Jacques said it was not a good omen."

Ruud frowned and looked up. "Jacques said it was not a good omen?" he repeated. "Jacques!" he shouted, startling me.

Jacques came running, wiping his wet hands on his shirt. He was smiling.

"You told Priya that finding a cat is a bad omen?" Ruud asked quizzically.

"No, did I say that?" he looked in my direction, confused. "I said that we usually don't make drums out of cat skin," he said, looking up as he tried to remember the exact words.

"Yes, that's what he said. You can't make drums out of cat skin," I added, remembering the conversation and feeling stupid.

"There's a difference between a cat being a bad omen and not making drums out of cat skin," Ruud said, looking warmly in my direction. He had caught my mistake but was not going to take that opportunity to ridicule me. "Just because your action did not fit your expectation does not mean that it is a bad omen. When disappointment takes over, then we really don't listen to the words, we start listening to the feelings. So in your disappointment of finding a cat, you changed Jacques' words into feelings of a bad omen."

I wanted to tell Ruud, that was how I have interpreted every disappointment in my life, as a curse, as a bad omen. I was so naïve and I never understood it.

"Finding a cat is not a bad omen. We usually do not make drums out of cat skin because the myth says that the cat never dies. Even when it is dead, it is not. It has the boon of nine lives. But on a rare day, some equally powerful soul finds its way into the blessing of the cat. You did. You found the cat, so you make the drum," Ruud explained.

"You mean the cat is not dead?" I asked, shifting uncomfortably in my chair. Stories of ghosts had always freaked me out and I remember having spent sleepless nights for weeks after watching a silly horror film on TV. I was not ready to deal with cat spirits in a strange land.

"The myth says that the cat does not die. That is what attracted your spirit to the cat. The others did not notice it, you did. The myth says that when one attracts a cat in his life, one activates the boon of nine lives. What that means is that with every setback you come back to life. That there will be no force that will destroy your spirit. Like the phoenix, you will come back," Ruud explained with a smile.

"So why doesn't everyone look for a cat?" I asked. After all, if this was its power, it would make sense for everyone to go after the cat.

"No one is told anything in advance. You have to be attracted towards it. When people learn that cat skin is not used in drums they accept it as a bad omen, without questioning, and move on. Not everyone is overtly curious like you are. And not everyone is brave to risk being wrong." Ruud looked very pleased with me. My shame, fear, and anger suddenly evaporated. By not being told about this in advance, I was allowed my own path, my own journey, my own experience. Everything cannot be divulged. Some things unfold in your path and they are important only to your learning. Not everyone finds the cat, so they don't realise its significance. Not everyone asks questions, so they never find the answers.

Ruud got up and walked towards the wheel barrows. He spoke with the men who had gathered there. Each one of them took hold of a wheelbarrow and began to walk towards the barn.

I was not needed in the making of the drum, I thought, else they would have called me. My nausea had gone and my head had cleared. It's funny how mental confusion causes physical discomfort—as soon as your head and emotions are sorted out, your body is free of the pain and dis-ease it had felt.

I went back to the cottage. I thought I would take a nap. I was not worried about oversleeping; I knew that when it was time I would wake up or be woken up. As I entered the room I heard loud snores emanating from Emma who was clearly fast asleep.

I slipped into the bed, cocooned myself under the sheets, and drifted into sleep despite the thunderous snores.

I did not sleep well. I had disturbing dreams. I heard heavy drums, like sinister percussions, getting louder and louder until I could actually feel the heat from the drummers' bodies and the vibrations of the drums. I woke up with a start, shivering. A line of sweat trickled down from my temple and ran alongside the edge of my cheek. I shivered. There was silence. Pin drop silence. My head felt heavy and I could feel the onset of a headache.

I peeled the blanket off me. "I need some fresh air," I mumbled to myself.

Any kind of anticipation or excitement disturbs my sleep. I recall the nightmares I used to have, of unknown men trying to kill me. The nightmares recurred on many nights after my boyfriend proposed to me. It was as though the universe was warning me that something was wrong. Why else would I randomly get nightmares just after one of the biggest days of my life? I was obviously in love and I was obviously looking forward to being married one day. Or was I?

"Something is wrong," I would tell my best friend every morning. "I get nightmares. It does not feel right. I know something bad is going to happen."

My friends could not digest such negative talk from a motivational speaker and trainer, so I kept my emotions to myself. It seemed that the people close to me could not differentiate between Priya, the person, and Priya, the corporate guru. To them, I was superhuman, extraordinary. I was IT. Only I knew how naive and lost I was.

The same is the dilemma of the elder sibling, the man of the house, the parent, and the boss. You are perceived only in that role, a figure of responsibility, and not as an individual with ordinary emotions and worries. Consequently, too much is expected of you and nobody knows how lost and helpless and lonely you are.

Fraught with worry, I would tell my best friend, Shaun, "I never get nightmares. Please pray everything goes right."

I loved Shaun. He understood my hopes and believed in all my dreams. He had faith in all the things I did and supported my schemes. "Everything will be all right," was his standard reassurance.

It was only on one fateful night that I found out about the other woman in my boyfriend's life. His ex-flame had not yet been blown out of his life. I was heartbroken, completely shattered. I told myself, "I knew it. I knew something bad would happen." That was by far the worst time of my life— breaking off with my boyfriend of many years, a man who I had blinded trusted with my heart and my life. What my friends and family could not handle was that Superwoman had lost. They were in denial that their pillar of strength had fallen.

I look back at those nightmares. I look back at the feeling that something was wrong. And sure, something was wrong. It had been wrong for a long time but I didn't know it. I was blind to all the signs. I was ignorant of all the scheming happening around me. My friends knew but I did not. It's great to be positive and hopeful but it's greater to be aware and diligent. The nightmares had been a warning. I am the kind of person who does not easily accept that something could be wrong. Being a hopelessly optimistic person I am often in denial. But I also know that reality is bigger than hope and that, in real terms, everything is all right.

I often wonder what would have happened if I had found out about the other woman after my marriage, and possibly, a child. It makes me shudder to think that I could have torn my baby's life apart because of my ignorance. It was a narrow escape for me. Nothing was really wrong, everything was right. Everything was headed in the right direction. Everything was pointed in the direction of my evolution. And what makes me Superwoman is that I have the courage to take bold decisions and be responsible for my life. I saw the reality and I took my chances and walked out.

I still could not shake off the sound of the drums. They sounded ominous, almost announcing the arrival of death. I was anxious and my stomach felt funny. I ran to the toilet.

Soon there was a loud knock on the door. "Ruud wants to see you," Emma said. I was happy she had learnt to knock but I wished she could have waited for me to come out.

I hurried out. My head was still heavy and was now pounding with pain. I picked up my coat and headed out to the garden.

The sun had already set and the sky was settling in to welcome the stars. In the flickering lamp light I could see Ruud, eyes closed in prayer, I thought. Mary had placed a pot of pansies on the table and it looked divine. I have always been fascinated by pansies. They have so much expression that sometimes I secretly speak to them. "You are crazy," Shaun would say, always so tolerant of my idiosyncrasies.

I sat opposite Ruud and he opened his eyes. "You have a headache?" he asked, looking at me. "Yes, a pounding headache," I said, squinting my eyes. Even the faint light from the lamp hurt my eyes and aggravated my headache.

"What does that mean?" Ruud asked.

"What does my headache mean?" I asked, frowning. Ruud nodded.

"I don't know. Maybe I am losing my brains," I laughed out loud. I was amazed that the headache had not dimmed my ability to laugh at myself. That was something I specialised in—having fun all by myself.

Ruud nodded, waiting for an answer.

"I don't know," I moaned. "I had a nightmare, and now, the headache. Every time I get a headache like this, something goes wrong."

"Oh!" Ruud exclaimed. "Tell me more." He was either interested or he was humouring me.

I started to laugh, I have no idea why. It's one of those times when you know that whatever you speak from here on will make no sense. I rubbed my eyes and patted my head hard. "I'm a tough cookie. I will be ok," I smiled. And I really felt a wee bit better.

"The human body is an amazing device," Ruud said, bringing me back to the conversation. "Pain is a gift. I don't understand why people run away from it. Can you imagine what would happen if you stub your toe on a sharp iron nail and it cuts into your skin but there is no pain?"

"I wouldn't know that I had cut my foot and I would continue to walk," I answered, deeply hooked on to what Ruud was saying.

"And by the time your wounded foot catches your attention you would have walked, miles, accumulated septic agents, dirt, and everything that will lead to gangrene, and eventually you would lose your foot if not your leg," Ruud said matter-of-factly. "So what is the role of pain here, my lady?"

"To get my attention to what is wrong, to get my attention to what is hurt," I replied.

"So that with your attention you can heal it and set it right," Ruud added, smiling at my intelligence.

"You have a headache. Something is certainly wrong, my love. And now is your chance to set it right." Ruud got up and whisked up a big leather bag. He took out a small drum with tightened leather on it. I recognised the white and golden fur—it was the wild cat. This was my drum. My headache disappeared.

"That's my drum," I said excitedly, like a school girl drooling over her birthday dress. I ran my fingers over the cat skin and I closed my eyes and blessed the spirit of the cat. May its nine lives, and transition, be worthy of glory and divinity. I was happy.

"This is your drum. Be careful, now is not the time to beat it. When you sleep, keep it under your bed. No one must touch it but you. Tomorrow we start the Drummer's ritual; that's when we will initiate it," Ruud instructed.

"Why must there be a tomorrow?" I thought. I am ready today. I hate waiting. I am a NOW person. I want everything now. My mother would call me an impatient soul and would often scold me for being so restless. The fact is that I am always ready to act, full of energy and spirit. Why wait for tomorrow? To me, every moment is the right moment. What I forget in the bargain is that some things take time and some things happen at their own time. The sun can't rise at my "now" just because I am excited. I must wait for morning. So I calmed down my spirit and decided to wait. Not that I had a choice anyway.

"Eat well and, most importantly, sleep well. Trust me, you will need all the energy you can muster for the ritual tomorrow. You need the strength of a man to part take in it. Work on your energy." Ruud touched my head and pulled me into a hug.

I liked Ruud. He was compassionate and very understanding. Is it age that makes men genuine? Or is it that some men evolve and others don't? I had never met a man as balanced, composed, and wise as Ruud. He had it all—good looks, the spiritual edge, and a very compassionate heart.

I was left enveloped in cigarette smell as Ruud walked away shouting something to Mary in Dutch.

Sitting at the garden table I was excited. I felt alive. Sleep was nowhere in sight. I knew I was going to be in trouble.

Anticipation always keeps me awake. I have spent nights wide awake in anticipation before my exams and barely made it to the examination hall the next day. The night before my first shoot I didn't sleep and had to put ice on my eyes because they were so puffy. I toss and turn all night, frittering away my energy which could be used more fruitfully. "How am I going to sleep tonight?" I shrieked in my head.

Dinner was light and quiet. Everyone was tired after the animal hunt. I too had been tired earlier, but now I was as fresh as the morning dew.

With no penalties and no dishes to wash I walked to the room—it was empty. Sain, Rick, and Emma were usually in the room before I was. They must be busy elsewhere I thought and climbed into bed. I picked a book from Emma's bedside table hoping it would help me sleep. Double checking that the drum was safe under my bed, I started to read.

My eyes moved over the words but my mind drifted

elsewhere. I had turned three pages but I hadn't read a thing. Frustrated, I shut the book and put it away.

I got out of bed and picked out my diary which I had made from trashed paper that Mary had given me. I started to write.

"I'm in anticipation of what will happen tomorrow. I'm here in a strange land, with strange people, doing strange things. I have never been so alive and so challenged before. My house, my people, my friends, my life, my memories all seem far away. Nothing here is familiar except my own stuck up self. I never really had to leave anyone or anything because I have carried everyone and everything with me, in my head. I want to be free. I don't want to have my head full of other people, their opinions or their expectations. I want to be free. I want my head in the right place, eager, alive, delighted and looking forward to life. I don't know what will happen in the drumming ritual but I would like to learn to play the drum. I don't know why it is a man's ritual and I don't know why I must want what I can't have. I don't know why I love challenges. I don't know why I grab every opportunity to stretch myself, my mind, my heart, my soul. I don't know why I am here. I don't know what I am looking for. All I know is that I want to be free. I don't even know what it means to be free. Maybe when I touch 'freedom', I will know. Maybe tomorrow, or another day."

My pen drifted loosely on the stapled pages. My eyes were heavy and my mind zeroing out. Writing is therapeutic. Thoughts keep running marathons in our heads. Out of one thought spring forth a thousand and very soon we are on a mental roller coaster. Writing brings out, in perspective, what looms in the head. I no longer had the desire to think or anticipate. I could see my thoughts on paper and I was at peace. Whether they made sense or not was irrelevant; they were out of my head and I was ready to sleep.

I slipped into the sheets, keeping the 'diary' under my pillow. No one had returned yet and I didn't care. I wanted to sleep. I bent over, checked on the drum, and closed my eyes with a smile on my face. I was ready . . . for the land of slumber.

I woke up in the morning. Daylight was just creeping into the room. I jumped out of bed and ran to the window. It was the most magical daybreak I had ever seen. Faint stars and a fading moon dotted a greyish blue sky. Birds chirped and drops of dew slithered down moist, green leaves. An eagle in flight was silhouetted against the morning sky. And then within seconds the sky grew lighter, the stars dimmed and out sprang the first ray of the sun. I closed my eyes and made a wish: "May my life on earth be one worthy of my spirit." I opened my eyes to a dance of life. Golden rays of the sun shone on the fields in the distance, the sky changed colours like a chameleon, and birds darted between trees amidst a melody of tunes. I stretched my arms and muttered out loud, "Good morning, World" knowing my energy would reach every atom on the planet.

I noticed that all the other beds were empty. That was strange. I peered under the bed to find my drum lying still and pretty. I bathed in a jiffy and wore the same old blue jeans with a clean white t-shirt. I didn't feel like weighing myself down with the coat so I decided to shiver my way through breakfast. I wanted to feel light and I was ready to deal with the cold.

No one was down for breakfast. I went into the kitchen and started the stove to make my coffee and warm some bread. I took my plate and went out into the garden. As I sat there sipping my coffee, I could see Ruud standing in the distance, facing the sun. He was moving very tai chi like—Ruud was doing the sun dance.

What a wonderful start to my day! Having breakfast in the garden on a beautiful morning and watching a man doing a sun dance. So much more enjoyable than catching the normally depressing breaking news on television and ruining the day!

Ruud finished his dance just as I finished my coffee. He walked in my direction, looking surprised. "You should have joined me," he said.

"I wanted to watch you," I winked with a smile.

"Did you sleep well?" Ruud asked, ignoring my flirtatious comment.

"Yes, I am surprised I slept so well. I am ready," I said cheerfully. I had surpassed my own expectations. I had broken a pattern and I was extremely proud of myself.

"Are you ready to go?" Ruud asked, standing beside me.

"Absolutely," I replied.

Ruud held me tightly by the shoulder and we walked towards the fields. Just a few meters away we entered the neighbouring field and I saw a stone and wood house. I had seen this house several times before. It looked abandoned and uninhabited. We walked towards it and I could feel the butterflies return to my stomach. My body was preparing for a transition and I could feel the signs. My soul was ready for liberation.

The house had a small garden. The flowers and the grass were in a sorry condition and I could see some spider webs gleaming in nooks and corners. We walked on the narrow pebbled path and reached the heavy teak wood door. Ruud pushed it open.

It was dark inside. I could hear Rick's voice. He emerged from a dimly lit room. He looked different. His body was bare except for a skin cloth around his waist. His hair was loose and he wore a white headband. The muscles of his sweat-soaked body gleamed. "We are ready," he smiled at Ruud and turned to me. "Are you?"

I didn't know what to say. I wanted to say no just for the fun of it but I realised this was not the time for fun.

"Yes, I am," I answered, still startled at Rick's nomadic look.

"Come with me," he said, moving towards a door on the right.

I followed. Rick opened the door to another room, completely bare except for a chair in the centre. There was some skin clothing on the chair. "Change into this. Only this." He looked at me to make sure I had understood. I nodded. Rick stepped back and went out of the room, gently shutting the door behind him.

I walked towards the chair and looked around the room. The ample use of rough wood gave it a rustic feel. There was a faint smell of polish. The chair was old and weathered, and on it lay a waistband and a long cloth that I assumed was meant to be tied around my chest like a tube bikini. There was also a white headband and a beaded armlet.

I wore the headband first, pulling my hair down punk-style. I picked up the waistband and wrapped it around my waist. It just about covered my butt. I folded the wrap-around band twice around my chest and knotted it firmly at the back. Neatly folding my clothes and placing them on the chair, I looked around for a mirror. I wanted to see how I looked in a skimpy skin bikini wrap-around topped with a multi-coloured armlet and a funky headband. I looked almost pagan, straight out of a Tarzan movie.

There was a light knock on the door as Rick asked, "Are you

ready?"

I walked to the door and opened it, striking a pose for Rick. He laughed and ruffled my hair. I struck his hand away. "You are spoiling my hairdo," I chuckled. Still smiling, Rick led the way to the main room.

He opened the door. The smell of strong musky incense came gushing out. I entered a smoky, dimly lit room and tried to adjust my eyes. There were four torches burning in the four corners of the room. A medicine man stood beside each torch with a large drum and gong. The medicine men were dressed in the same attire as mine except for the top band. They looked like white-skinned African drummers. Ruud was sitting in prayer on what looked like a bear skin rug, legs folded.

Rick beckoned me to sit opposite him. I obeyed, my heart racing. And suddenly an eerie feeling crept into my body: I had forgotten my drum. I looked up at Rick who smiled an "everything will be all right" smile that I had often seen on Shaun.

Ruud picked up the owl feather fan that lay in his lap and touched my forehead with it. "I'm sorry, Ruud, I forgot the drum," I wanted to tell him, but I could not utter a word.

"Drumming is a man's ritual, you know that," Ruud began. "This ritual is performed to free a man's spirit. It is only a man with a liberated spirit who can maintain and sustain the demands of his multiple relationships and duties on planet earth. A liberated spirit is that which recognises its purpose and moves through relationships and circumstances seeking its fulfilment. A liberated soul is a force; it is unstoppable. A liberated soul is that which is bigger than the big and uses its power to fulfil its purpose. May you be the powerful man-woman you are! May the man in you liberate the woman you are through this ritual."

"The ritual ends when you are free and that is something you will control. We are here to serve you, to be a medium for you to reach the plane where you set yourself free. It is an honour. Meet you on the other side." Ruud got up and in a few seconds I got up too.

"You will now choose your medium." He looked around at all the men and beckoned me to choose my medium, meaning one of the men.

I did not understand what choosing the medium meant but I had to choose between the six men in the room. Without any hesitation I chose Ruud. He and Rick exchanged a glance; I think they knew that I would choose him.

Ruud was standing in front of me. He took my hand, saying, "You will lie down here on the bear skin and we will start the ritual. The ritual ends when you are free. You decide when it ends." I nodded and sat down on the bear skin again.

How in the world will I know I am free? I only know what it is to be trapped. What if I goof up? What if I make a mistake? What if I am not free but think I am free? I didn't like this anymore. I wanted to go home. I began to indulge in my spontaneous response to confusion: "I want to go home. I want to be alone." But before I could verbalise my intention, the drums had started beating.

The drums were so loud and powerful that I was locked in the vibration. I could no longer sit, I wanted to lie down. My head touched the ground and my body began to vibrate with the rhythm of the drum beats. My heart beat, my pulse, my blood flow were frenzied, in total disarray. There was no rhythm in my body other than the vibration of the drums. With every beat of the drums the world fell further and further away. There was only sound and vibration until finally I became the vibration. I could not focus anymore. Everything seemed a blur as I closed my eyes.

I felt a line of feathers spanning my whole body. Normally it would have tickled me but with so much vibration it felt as though I was being packed in. Then a spray of cold water made me leap out of my skin, and my eyes flew open. I felt like a hostage in a crime film being splashed with cold water after a sequence of torture. As I opened my eyes, I could see a blurry figure standing on top of me, legs apart. It was Ruud. He appeared like a gigantic monster. He bent down with knees on either side of my waist. He then spread his arms on either side of my shoulders and straightened his legs, moving beyond my feet. His body was now parallel to mine. The smell of heavy musky incense poured in. His sweat fell on my face and I could see his face vibrate to the beat of the drums. The heat from Ruud's body was penetrating mine. He was looking deep into my eyes. I was frightened.

What was going to happen? What was he going to do? Millions of images of insane sexual rituals ran through my head. I had read stories and articles about such things and now I was trapped in that very scene. I wanted to run away but the vibration of the drums had locked in my body and I was unable to move. I felt trapped.

Ruud must have read the terror in my eyes. He must have also understood that I was telling him not to mess with me. Suddenly he closed his eyes and as though a plug was pulled I closed mine too. And in that instant a heavy weight came crashing on me. Ruud. All 6 feet 3 inches of this gigantic man totally engulfed my petite form. I was pinned down, confined and immobile under Ruud.

Ruud's chest smothered my face and my feet were painfully pinned under his calves. I could not breathe. There was a bulky sweaty man lying on me. I was choking. My ribs were crushed, my lungs had no room to expand, and my nostrils were blocked. I felt I was going to die. I was certainly going to die.

I wanted to push Ruud off me. I was a petite woman. This was murder. I could not breathe. I could not speak. I could not move. I was going to die. This was a huge mistake. I should never have come here. I should have gone back. I would never again move into uncharted territory. I should have minded my own business.

"Noooooooooooooooooooooooooooooo," I screamed but the sound only reverberated within my head. There was silence. No drums. No sound. No light. No weight. No sight. No sensation. That was the silence I felt. There was nothing. Just total silence. I had died.

My last moments were regret. Plain and simple regret. My life was a flood of regret. It was about what I did not do or should not have done. The sum total of my whole life was Regret.

The light returned. I could see again but there was no me. I could see the drummers beating the life out of the drums, sweating profusely. I could see the flames of the torches vibrating violently to the rhythm of the beats. I could see Rick moving furiously across the room in long dance-like strides, splashing water on the parched bodies of the drummers from a skin bag wrapped around his shoulder. I could see Ruud lying on me, still as a rock. I could not see my body. It was engulfed under Ruud.

What was happening? Where was I? Who was I? I could see the entire scene but I could not hear the clamour. It was as though someone had pressed the mute button on a very violent war.

I hung in there in the room, random thoughts of death flashing in my mind. Someday all of us will die; we will be free from our bodies and from human responsibility. When that day will dawn is not known to anyone. That is a day no one looks forward to. Death is taboo. Death is unwelcome.

Death is fear. Death is worse than life. Death is an end that no one is ready to meet. But death is inevitable.

And it had been easy. It had taken less than three minutes to die, to break free. But those three minutes reduced thirty years of my existence to regret. It reduced my life into a meaningless, useless waste of time. I did not know which was worse, living or dying, because both seemed the same at that moment.

I began to reflect on my life and what I had done in all the years I had lived. What was my life really about? It was the same madness of the men beating the drums furiously. Drums I couldn't hear. It was the same madness of this man splashing water on the dehydrated bodies of the drummers. It was the same madness of a man lying purposefully on my body to liberate my soul. What had I been doing all my life?

I hung on in this silent space asking an account of my life from myself! I had no account. I had nothing to show, except regret. I had nothing to analyse except my own stuck up, fearful, laid back approach and I was amazed that people found me extraordinary.

I could see the lie behind the truth that people saw in me. Right now the people were not there, it was I facing my lies. The lie that I was weak; the lie that I was cheated; the lie that I was not good enough; the lie that I was not loved, that I was not supported, that I was not important. Those were my lies to me and I lived them every single day of my life.

I saw a life lived in ignorance, sheer ignorance. Weakness is a sign of ignorance. Sadness is a sign of ignorance. Fear is a sign of ignorance. I had spent my whole life in ignorance.

What I so desperately needed and yearned for right now was a chance to set it all right; to set myself all right. I knew that there was only one life, the one I built. Whether it was lived in ignorance or in awareness, it was a life built by me. I knew that there was only one future, the one I chose for myself. I knew there was only one truth, the one I told myself. All I needed was one chance to set my life right. Right now I was a small speck of regretful awareness.

All I craved was one more chance. A few more hours, a few more days, a few more years, and I knew I would leave the world in joy and not regret. Just one more chance.

"Ruud, get off me," I screamed against the beat of the drums, the shrill timbre of my voice breaking the vibration of the pounding gongs. Suddenly everything came to a halt. The drums stopped, the vibration continuing to resonate for some time. Ruud's body broke free of the vibration and so did mine, and I could feel the synergised beating of our hearts loud and clear. A shiver came over me and shook Ruud's body. He rolled over like a log of wood and fell on my right. I was miraculously free.

I was free. I was alive. I was given my chance to live. I was given my chance to start and end in joy.

I began to gasp for breath and felt ice cold water splashed on my face and body. I began to tremble violently like a fish out of water. I tried to open my eyes but couldn't. I tried to move but I couldn't. It was like a futile attempt to wake up from a bad dream. I could feel that same struggle, only this time my struggle was to come alive.

I felt Ruud's hands covering my body with a skin blanket. My shivers began to calm. Cold water was poured on my head and I no longer felt the need to struggle. I was here. I was calm.

I don't know how long I lay there. It was a zero state. I was a clean slate; a clean canvas. I felt like a person with no past, only the present and a future to conquer. I felt new. I felt free.

I slowly opened my eyes. The room was dark and silent. The drummers had gone and so had Rick and Ruud. I tried to get up and fell limp several times before I could sit up. There was a tub of water with a glass next to me. Instinctively I reached out and filled the glass with water and started to sip it. It was a pungent liquid and it pumped life into my body in an instant.

I stood up, legs still shaking, and walked towards the door. It was dark outside. No sound. Only silence. I groped my way to the room where I had changed, and pushed open the door. The room was still lit with a wick lamp. Outside the window was a scene of stars in the night sky. I felt as though I had spent an eternity in the process; whether it was the same day or days later, I couldn't tell, I was still disoriented.

I changed into my clothes, neatly laying the sweat soaked skin on the chair.

I went out of the house, tracing my steps back on the pebbled path. The cottage was lit in the distance with smoke emerging from the chimney. I walked towards it with small thoughtful steps.

The sky was an umbrella speckled with stars. I marvelled at its enormity; the universe was so large, and I, such a small being with my own hang ups. My neck was paining with the sudden lifting of my head and I lay down on the grass. I could see Saturn, the planet I used to see so often through the telescope. I loved Saturn; a living planet with clearly visible rings. It fascinated me. In an instant I could see myself sitting on the outer ring of Saturn. "A soul can sit anywhere, even if the ring is a cloud of dust," I chuckled to myself. And from my celestial perch I looked down upon this little girl sleeping on the grass; a girl with a list of petty complaints and regrets about the world. The list is so irrelevant when you see yourself from the vision of an ever expansive universe. The only language that the universe understands is joy; the only prayer it responds to is love. And when one lives one's life with joy and love, one discovers its universal power, its liberated soul.

I smiled. I was free.

I got up, realising how ravenous I was. I walked towards the cottage with light steps. As I pushed open the door the aroma of freshly cooked food hit my nostrils.

"You must be hungry," Ruud turned in his chair. It was the same Ruud who had almost crushed me to death, only now he wore spectacles on his nose and khaki attire, with his hair neatly tied in a ponytail.

"You bet I am," I laughed and plonked right next to him.

"Make sure you beat your drum tonight before you sleep. That will complete the ritual," Ruud said. He held me in an embrace, one that is exchanged between two liberated souls.

I ate to my heart's content.

I was free.

My experiences 'lessoned' for you:

···> If you love what you do then you won't have to work a single day of your life.

···> You know more than you give yourself credit for. You already know what is right and that's how you recognise it when you see it.

···> In the bargain of give and take, give doesn't make you less and take doesn't make you more. It's just a shift in possession and a shift in perception.

···> You should not see your reality through someone else's eyes. The only person who truly knows and can build your reality is you.

···> Life is the meaning you assign to your experiences. When you change the meaning you change the impact that experience has on you.

···> You must listen fully without the interference of your own limited conclusions. The absence of it marks the beginning of misunderstanding.

···> It is crazy to believe without inspection and to act without reason.

···> It is always better to tell your story in honesty than have someone else narrate his interpretation of it.

···> Writing brings out in perspective what looms in your head. When you can see your thoughts on paper, there is peace.

···> The answer for confusion is clarity and that is seldom found in running away.

···> The lies you tell yourself become your truth. Weakness is a lie. The only truth is boundless power.

···> The only consequence of ignorance is regret. To live in awareness and responsibility leads to a life well lived.

The Spiritual Walk

I had liked Martin from the day I saw him at the Sweat Lodge. One look at him and I knew he was the one. I never believed in love at first sight until I met Martin. When my friends spoke about love at first sight I often wondered if they were talking about love or about loving the sight. What really is love? I was often confused. True love is when you love what is, not how it seems. What we so loosely define as love is just admiration for the overtly pleasant. That is why, after the first flush of excitement, when the person's real character takes shape in our reality the love abruptly ends. That was what happened in my relationships. The love came to an end and none of the superficial trappings of beauty could save it.

A person may be attracted to beauty but there must be something more than mere looks to hold that attraction. If not, attraction may get transformed into revulsion. A strong relationship can be built only when one gets past the attraction stage and is able to understand the true nature of the other. The trick is to wait until this point to meaningfully say, "I love you".

But my feelings for Martin were more than just mere attraction, or so I told myself. I could see the sincerity and wisdom in his eyes. "He is the one," my heart said. But I decided to wait a while before admitting to myself that I was in love. When the eyes are blinded by beauty, all seems well. When you see a beautiful sunset, your head ache disappears and all seems beautiful in your world. That is what beauty does to you. It brings a temporary feeling of well being. But if you wait and watch you see the different phases of the sun. The innocent sunrise turning into raging noon heat, to the gentle setting in the evening leaving you in total darkness for a long time before it raises its innocent head again at dawn. That is the cycle of the sun, the lover, and life.

Martin was different, my mind protested. But I decided to watch him a bit more before I admitted to myself that I was in love. "I am in admiration," I consoled myself.

I was sitting on the window sill, still in my pyjamas, shivering occasionally in the morning chill. I was in no hurry. Today was the day off. It was the day you could choose what you wanted to do and what you wanted to eat. "It is your day," Kahuna had said.

I wanted to spend the day with Martin. I could see him in the garden playing with the neighbour's dogs. He was tall, lean, and gorgeous. He ran across with three dogs clinging on to him. I laughed heartily when one overly large sheepdog pinned him to the ground—I could only see a pair of blue jeans peeking out from under three playful, excited canines.

I decided to get ready quickly and run down to ask Martin out before he made his choices for the day. In fifteen minutes I was ready in a nice skirt with a dainty top hidden under the gigantic fur coat.

I ran down to the garden. Martin was red with all the running and was sitting at the garden table sipping a cup of steaming coffee. I have made my choice," I announced without wasting time. "I know how I want to spend my day today," I said, approaching him.

"Oh, that's great. And you seem to be dressed for it," Martin smiled, acknowledging that I looked pretty; at least that's what I told myself. My soul danced with joy at the thought. It's amazing how we construe people's words to mean what we want them to mean. We live our life through our own expectations. We are never really victims; we bring things upon ourselves through our erroneous interpretation of people's words. Because I was beaming with love I could only interpret everything Martin said or did as love. That is the "love is foolish" we refer to. The truth is we are sometimes foolish enough to weave our desires in other people's communication and then feel good or bad about it. Martin did not say I was pretty but I chose to interpret his words to meet my desire because I was in love with him.

"I'm going to spend the day with you," I said slightly demanding as though I had made a choice for both of us.

"Great. And what would you like to do?" Martin asked without any resistance.

I loved it. That was a sign already. He had agreed to spend the day with me. Maybe he was really fed up of his fiancée. Maybe she didn't treat him right. Maybe this was my chance. At that moment it did not cross my mind that I was treading the same path my ex boyfriend had. Although the pain of my own break up was fresh in my mind, the devastation I could cause by breaking up Martin's engagement never occurred to me. I was in love. Maybe my ex boyfriend too had been in love, I thought. And maybe it had never occurred to him that he would cause me so much hurt. Life is strange; we acknowledge our pain but we often do not see our own actions damaging the life of another.

I was excited. "Anything you say. I'm new to the place. I don't know what would be nice to do," I said. I was making plans and I was happy.

"You are extremely special, you know that?" Martin said. Was it love I heard in his voice? I couldn't tell and I didn't care. "Let me take you on a spiritual walk today. Choose your time and I will be there to get you," Martin smiled.

"A spiritual walk?" I queried. "What is that?" I was excited but slightly confused.

"Yes, a spiritual walk. You start the walk with a question and you end with an answer. You choose where and when you want to walk. The world is your option," he winked.

I wanted to choose Venice. I had always wanted to go there with my soul mate. I wished Venice was a walk away. "I would like to go into the forest, in the night, under the stars," I said.

I could see a startled expression on Martin's face. "In the night? Are you sure?" he asked, as though he had heard me wrong.

"Yes," I beamed. "I would like to take a spiritual walk with you in the forest in the night under the stars."

"To be honest I have never led a spiritual walk in the night in the forest, so this would be my first time. But like I said, it's your walk and it's your choice. I will meet you at 8 o'clock right here. Be ready!" Martin said, gulping down the last of his coffee. He got up and ran towards the madly racing dogs.

"Wow," my soul smiled. "A spiritual walk with Martin tonight. This is divine."

I spent the whole day lazing, either napping in bed or lying on the grass watching the clouds change shape in the sky. As evening approached the clouds became a little thicker and darker and a wave of chill began to build up. Was there going to be a storm? My heart sank.

"Nooooo!" I raised my fist threateningly at the sky. "Not tonight! Any night, anywhere, but not tonight!" Before I knew it, the heavens responded defiantly to my rage, and I felt the first drops of water on my face. It had begun to drizzle.

I covered my head and ran inside the cottage. I spent the entire evening sitting at my window watching the downpour and beseeching the clouds to clear up by 8 o'clock. Alas, the universe was not at my command. It was doing what needed to be done. And my walk and my big night had no meaning in the context of universal laws.

It was 7.45 p.m. and the clouds were not yet spent. I was upset and angry, and I could feel a whole gush of tears welling up in my eyes. This was my only chance with Martin and the stupid rain was messing it up. It was as though the universe was getting some cheap pleasure out of making life difficult for me.

"This always happens to me," I thought. "I am the unlucky one. Fortune never favours me. Every time I want something really badly, something happens to take it away from right under my nose." Tears began to flow down my cheeks and I began to sob violently.

I remembered the time I had worked so hard on a school project, by far a work of art, but the school president's daughter got the award for a mediocre one. Life was not fair, I had learnt early. I was the super kid in college but the guys went after the dumber girls. My intelligence had not served me. Life was not fair, I had reaffirmed whenever I did not have my way. I had to work hard ever since I was in my teens and I never really enjoyed the carefree life of a typical teenager. While my friends were out partying, I was preparing and working to teach my set of students. And just when I had found the man of my dreams and knew I would be happy ever after, there was someone better than me who had got his attention. Life was not fair, I was convinced. And I had begun to believe that I was particularly unlucky.

I heard a knock on the door and wiped my eyes. It was Mary. Without opening the door she shouted, "Martin is here to get you." And her steps faded away.

Martin was here? He made it in the rain? Oh my god! I ran helter-skelter. I had not decided what to wear, my eyes were puffy, I looked miserable. I heard another knock. "Are you ready?" asked Martin.

"Yes," I shouted. "Will be out in a minute." I slipped on my jeans and my running shoes, quickly splashed water on my face, gave myself a dazzling smile, picked up my coat and ran out.

Martin was standing at the door, wearing muddy ankle boots. He wore a windcheater with a hood and his face was wet from the rain. "You have stirred up quite a storm, lady," he chuckled as he saw me.

"Here," he said, handing an over sized jacket and ankle boots. "You will need these for your, umm, spiritual walk in the forest under the stars." And we both burst out laughing.

I slipped on the jacket and the boots, Martin took my hand and we stepped outside. It was dark and it was raining. The grass was no longer visible and I splashed into puddles with every step. It was as cold as in Antarctica, I thought. The wind made it worse, slamming the raindrops on my face. I struggled to wipe them off, much like a wiper on a car on a rainy day.

"We will walk to the highway and take a bus twenty minutes to the onset of the woods nearby," Martin said, increasing his pace and almost pulling me along. "We don't want to miss the bus," he explained, now breaking into a run.

I was running in wet and muddy fields with thunder and lightning over my head and ice drops piercing my face. My hands were frozen long ago and I could feel the cold despite the warm jacket I was wearing.

We reached the highway, covered with mud up to our knees, faces and hair wet, and goose bumps all over. My teeth were chattering. Suddenly I saw two yellow lights emerging from the darkness far away.

"We made it," Martin smiled.

The bus stopped to pick us up. It was empty. We both walked to the front and sat there.

"So how did you do this?" Martin asked, wiping his face with the sleeve of his coat.

"How did I do what?" I asked, not knowing what he was referring to.

"How did you manage to create this downpour?" Martin asked innocently yet very curiously. There was no doubt in his head that the storm and the rain was not an accident. He knew I had done it and he wanted to know how and why.

"You are saying that in some way I influenced and directed the storm clouds over our village and instructed them to pour at a time when I had chosen my spiritual walk?" I was amused. Martin was not.

"Yes, and I want to know why you did it," he said.

"I have no idea what you are talking about, Martin," I responded and we both were silent for the rest of the journey.

Did I create the storm? The question ran in my head a million times and I could not find a single reasonable answer.

The bus came to a halt. Martin took my hand and we leapt off the bus into nowhere. We were on the highway with a sort of dense forest on both sides. We stood there as the sky thundered and the downpour became heavy. In a mocking way it seemed like an auspicious start to our spiritual walk.

"Which way should we go?" Martin asked me.

"I don't know," I said. "I have no idea."

"This is your walk. You decide the direction."

"But what if we get lost?" I asked, unable to hide my horror. I was beginning to feel uncomfortable and there were butterflies in my stomach. This was more exciting than I had imagined; being lost in the jungle with Martin was an interesting thought.

"We will eventually find a way," Martin smiled.

I had learnt by now not to argue. Martin had obviously done spiritual walks before and he knew the process. I decided to obey without thinking too much. I did not know what lay ahead; I was treading into unknown territory. I had no idea which direction to pick. My destination was as unclear as my journey. The only thing I knew for certain was that with every step I would find out. And such is life. You never know what lies ahead unless you move ahead. And the good part is if you don't like what you see, you can always change direction. That is the gift, the gift of choice, at every given step.

I looked on both the sides of the highway; the forest looked eerie and the darkness and the rain did not help. This was a sinister opposite to what I had planned.

"Let's go to the left," I told Martin and we crossed the road and entered a thicket of trees.

It was dark, like the scene you would expect in a horror film involving unfriendly ghosts and vengeful spirits.

"I don't know where to go," I said, not letting go of Martin's hand. This was not my version of a night out with a man I deeply admired.

"You are in charge here," Martin said, gently freeing his hand. "I'm merely your companion, your alter ego in the journey. I follow where you take me only to help you see the light you have been keeping away from yourself and the world."

I felt fear creeping up. It was a scary night. It was dark. I didn't know what kind of forest this was. I didn't know what wild animals lived here. I didn't know if it was swarming with spirits or cannibals out on a hunt, waiting for some foolish kid to decide to take a spiritual walk at this insane hour.

Something darted on the path in front of me and I yelped, almost jumping into Martin's arms.

"I'm sorry," I said sheepishly because I had almost knocked Martin to the ground. He regained his balance. "No worries," he said. "It was probably a wild cat on the prowl." And we continued to walk.

An angry bat flapped its wings furiously and made a cry, dashing from one tree to another. I freaked. With another yelp, I jumped on Martin again. This time he caught me before I took both of us down. "I'm so sorry, Martin," I said, not knowing how to apologise.

This spiritual walk would certainly give me a heart attack and I would die, I thought. My spirit would be released in the walk, maybe that's why they called it a spiritual walk.

"Are you sure you are sorry? Are you sure you won't jump on me again?" Martin asked.

I was confused. I did say I was sorry. Of course it was more of a polite, instinctive gesture than an actual, deep feeling of remorse. And Martin had confronted me. How rude, I thought.

"If you are not certain of your own edginess, it's best you don't apologise. Because when you apologise what you are saying is that it won't happen again and that you have understood your mistake. But to apologise and continue to repeat the same act reduces the value of your apology and makes it a mere fake formality," Martin said, looking me straight in the eye. I tried to focus on him but the shifting forest was altering my heart beat and freaking me out.

"If you are uncertain of your actions and have not yet confronted your fears, it's best you get my permission to seek shelter with me. But you jump on me and apologise, and then I give up my guard because you apologise, and you jump on me again. And then you apologise once more and repeat your actions. This way you are hurting me and yourself too," Martin said, now nudging me to walk on.

"So what must I do?" I asked with a tremor in my voice.

"Tell me what you feel, be honest, not apologetic," Martin said, gently touching my shoulder.

How many times we apologise just as a way out of the discomfort of being confronted! It is easier to say sorry and get out of the situation than face the situation itself. And how many times in my life I must have apologised without even having understood the source of my actions. And with every apology that was not confronted, I repeated the same action again and again.

Once, in a fit of rage over some trivial issue, I had stormed out of the house only to return and find my mother crying. I had apologised and consoled her; I would never do it again, I had promised. Only a few weeks later I had walked out of the house again and come back with another "sorry I won't do this again". This continued until it didn't even make sense to apologise any more. I would come back in silence, my self esteem lowered and my relationship with my mother stretched even further. Like most people, I had sought the easy way out. I had apologised mechanically when I should have tried to understand the cause for the apology.

"I'm afraid, Martin," I said, mustering up some courage. "The darkness freaks me out. I'm terrified of the dark. Even at home I sleep with the lights on all night."

"Then why did you choose the night?" I could see Martin smiling as though he knew why I had made the choice but was excited about me discovering it for myself.

"I love the starry sky. It reminds me that there is a whole big universe out there. There could be other planets with life forms, there is a higher intelligence out there, and I want to meet them. I want to communicate with them. I want to go there. I want to see the universe. The night sky opens the doorway to my imagination and I secretly find myself travelling through galaxies and planets. I want to be connected. I want my spiritual walk to lead me to that door which opens to a more intelligent and compassionate world." I was so surprised at what I had just said that I forgot my fear of the dense, dark forest.

"You can only know more if you become more. Your growth is proportionate to your world. When you grow, so does your world. When you grow, so does your love for the world. And when you grow, the universe grows with you.

There is a higher intelligence out there, and to be worthy of their attention and calling you have to ignite that higher intelligence within you. You have to free your spirit of the mindless impositions and the meaningless fears you have covered it with," Martin said.

He stopped. Taking my hand he asked, "Which is the darkest spot that you can see from here?"

I turned around, drawing myself as close to Martin as I could. Darkest spot? Everything around was dark, almost pitch black. Suddenly lightning lit up the path. Everything around me looked greyish black; the trees, tinted silver by the lightning, took human forms to mock me. And then it was dark again. I tried to strain my eyes, my heart racing; I could spot the darkest spot.

It was a large bent-over bush. Under the bush was the darkest dark that I could locate. "Right there," I pointed it out to Martin.

"Great, go experience the dark. Go to the bush and face the darkness," Martin said, letting go of my hand and giving me a gentle nudge.

Familiar, fearful voices began whispering in my head: "There is no force on planet earth that will take me into the dark. I can't do it. I will die. The ghosts will kill me. The wild animals will strike. The cat will steal my spirit. The leopard will chew off my arm. The bear will rip my head off. The witch will capture me and boil me in a cauldron along with other animals. The cannibals will trap me and throw me in a dungeon and eat my flesh. The ghost will blow and burn my flesh and turn my bones to dust. I will die." I cringed. Within a few seconds I must have died a thousand deaths. But I knew that if I did not face the darkness I would be carrying an empty, spiritless body around for the rest of my life.

I walked cautiously towards the bush. I did not turn back although I wanted to run for my life. I had half a mind to abandon Martin. "Screw him, I want to go back," I thought. But I walked a few more steps.

The bush was fifteen feet away. There were shades of darkness around it but it was darkest at the bottom where there was zero light. I looked at the bush; I stared at it with a blank mind. Not a single thought crossed my mind, almost as though I had no mind at all. I was only an observer. I looked at the form of the bush; it was dense with broad, tightly knit leaves; the kind that hosts a whole new world under its shade. No fruits, no flowers. My attention moved downwards to where the real darkness lay. I took a few more steps forward and sat down on my haunches to look at what was under. I saw two gleaming eyes staring right at me. With one shriek a wild cat darted out of the bush and scrambled into another. I sat there motionless. Can you imagine I had scared the living daylights out of a cat? I peered into the darkness and magically I could catch sight of the trunk of the bush. I could see some growth under there, the branches guarding the privacy of the undergrowth. My feet began to tingle and I could not sit anymore. I got up. One more look at the bush. It was just a bush. A bush in the dark.

It's not that the bush loved the dark; the bush was as much in darkness as the rest of the forest was. The bush was as much at the mercy of darkness as I was. Darkness is not something that characterises life; it is a phenomenon that life lives by. Darkness is something we survive by not freaking out. Darkness is something we outlive by not empowering our fears and internal demons. Darkness is the absence of light. Darkness is not the opposite of light.

I had never looked at darkness that way. Darkness is not a character, it's only a phase. Darkness is transition. It's temporary. To define darkness and to fight it is so futile because come morning it will go away. Just like you cannot fight the sun, you cannot fight its absence.

I could not believe this but I suddenly felt at peace.

I turned around. Martin was standing motionless. I walked towards him with more confidence in my being and Martin could sense that. He gave me a warm hug and I could feel the water squeeze out of our jackets. He did not say a word but I understood that he was proud of me.

We walked further. I led the way into the darkness. I did not know where I was going but I knew I was getting somewhere, and that in itself gave meaning to my journey.

"So what is your question?" Martin asked. "The spiritual walk is an answer to a question. What is yours?"

"I don't get success easily. I always have to struggle. I have to struggle and work hard to the point that I almost crumble and give up; and right when I am taking the u-turn, the world opens up. Why are there so many struggles? I hate it. Why can't the world acknowledge the fact that I am hard working and sincere? So much time would be saved. By the time I will actually get down to winning people's confidence and starting my work, life will end. Life is passing me by. Why can't I just get it? Why must there be a fight?" I said this all in one breath and I must have been loud because some birds began to caw angrily from the nearby trees.

"Shhh, sorry," I said, apologising to them, and Martin laughed loudly. "Shhh, sorry," he imitated me, putting his finger on his lips.

"You are a fun soul," he said, meaning it. "Can you define struggle?" Martin asked in the same breath.

"Struggle means hard work. Struggle means long hours of work. Struggle means when people don't understand the value of my work. Struggle means when people don't appreciate my work. Struggle means when the result of my work is obstructed by the mal intentions of others. Struggle means getting cheated when my intentions are good. I don't want to struggle anymore," I said in a stern voice. I was certainly fed up of being fed up.

"You mean you don't want to work hard and you don't want to work long hours?" Martin asked. "You don't look like a lazy girl to me," he winked in the dark.

"No, I want to work hard and I love working long hours but it's when people put obstacles in my way and hold me back that I get frustrated. I want to move ahead, at lightning pace, but people just won't let me," I complained, not about a particular issue but about life in general.

"You know what I love about you the most? That you think ahead of your time. You think ahead of anyone's time. You are gifted and you are blessed. Some people have created such unfortunate circumstances for themselves that they can't even see their present clearly let alone understand your vision and your aspirations. Your work must first serve you. When your work is for others alone, you will suffer due to the acceptance of the world or lack of it. Most commercial tycoons suffer spiritually because their produce does not serve them. Their destiny lies in the world's acceptance of their product and that is where most of the economic funds are transferred—in changing people's mindsets, and in making them see the use of a certain product so that a certain someone can be successful. That's not evolution and that's not spiritual growth. When you work and you produce, does that benefit you? If the whole world refuses to accept your work, does it still serve you?" Martin asked.

"Yes, I am the greatest beneficiary of what I do. When I learn, I grow. And I am compelled to share that knowledge and wisdom with others. That's my business," I explained. I was taken aback with this little realisation.

"So if no one came to your seminars any more, would your work still benefit you?" Martin asked.

"Yes, I am a student for life. I love learning. I love travelling. I absolutely love my work. In fact I never intended to be a speaker. I speak for the love of it and I also happen to get paid for it. It's that simple. Even if people didn't pay me, I would still speak," I expressed earnestly.

"Then how does other people's approval or disapproval matter? Have you ever been in love? Did you need other people's permission to love someone? Did you ever need another's approval in expressing your love to your special someone? Did you not cross every hurdle that came your way in spending time with that loved someone? Did it even matter who was in the way? Or was what mattered most the person waiting at the other end? People have never understood lovers. Speak to a revolutionary and he will tell you his lonely tales. Speak to a company CEO and he will tell you about his moments in solitude. Speak to the preacher, the son of God, the Buddha, Prophet Mohammad and they will tell you that they were the greatest beneficiaries of their own life. Whether people follow or understand is never in your control. People need to test whether what you have to offer is for real before they can trust you with their dreams and their life. And once you pass that test, the world will open its arms to you. But to pass that test, you will need to love the world. And that cannot happen if you think that the world is against you. The world is waiting for you. The world needs you. People have just been disappointed one too many times by other misled souls and they are just testing if you are for real.

"But the bottom line is, if you were to die tomorrow without having spread your message to the world, would the life you spent have any value for you?" Martin asked.

"Yes. Because of my work I have the respect of all the people I know. I am a better person and no matter how much I deny it, I love myself," I sighed.

"Who is the keeper of your success? Who decides your success? How would you know you are successful?" Martin asked curiously.

"I would know I am successful when I meet the result of my efforts. I want to reach out to every person on the planet and tell them that they are loved, that I believe in them, that everything will be ok, that life is beautiful."

"So why aren't you doing it? To love someone and to reach out to someone does not need state permission or a license of approval. You can do it right now in this moment," Martin said matter-of-factly.

Why had I never thought of this before? The answer was right there. It was as simple as it was divine and yet it had never occurred to me. I have spent years in pain and contempt not knowing that success was so simple. I did not need anyone's permission to be successful. If my work was serving my spiritual growth and also liberating others in the bargain then I was a success.

I had so many mixed emotions for Martin—love, admiration, respect, desire and they all were real. I guess we can only feel for another in the capacity of who we are. In knowing him, I was getting to know myself.

"You are so much like me," Martin said, as though he had the exact same emotions about me. "You are so much like me and I love you as much as I love myself. And I want you to know that you will feel my embrace every time I close my eyes in prayer."

Martin had taken the overused and overrated emotion of

love and given it supreme place—the place where no force can touch, move, or destroy it, and that is the place of prayer and intention.

I knew Martin was the one but I also knew now that I was the one I had been waiting for. I was who I had yearned for. I was the company I sought. I was the friend I desired. I was the lover, I was the mate, I was the companion, and I was the me I was looking for.

I was found. I had found myself.

"I want to go back," I turned to Martin.

"I'm following you, dearest one. Take us back," Martin shrugged.

I turned to the right and walked in knowingness. I did not know the way out but I knew I would get there. Out was not the way in. And the "out spot" would not be the "in spot". I would soon be out and there would be a whole different world waiting for me. Why would I ever want to go back to the place where I got in from? Out is a new world. There is no point hanging on to the security and familiarity of in. In was the past. Out was the future. My future.

We soon emerged in a clearing in an open field. There was some light in the distance. We were out.

"Let's approach the light and ask someone where we are," I said to Martin. I was totally in control and I was enjoying my newfound power. Martin raised his hands like a slave at my mercy.

As we stepped out into the fields and left the forest behind, as if by magic, the sky cleared up. The clouds parted and beautiful twinkling stars emerged. I sighed, looking up. The sky was so crystal clear, it took my breath away. "I will grow with the universe," I said to myself.

The light came from a beautiful cottage at the edge of the forest. It nestled there in the darkness, emitting its light, inviting lost wanderers like us for direction and comfort. The man in the cottage was amused to see us. "You bring good weather. Just a few minutes ago it was raining. Look at the beautiful sky your brought. How did you do that?" he asked, looking intently in my direction.

I smiled. "I'm lucky and I carry my luck wherever I go," I giggled like a little schoolgirl.

We found the highway a few meters away and waited for the bus.

"How did I create the storm?" I asked myself aloud.

"We lead ourselves where our highest lesson lies. You needed the storm for you to realise your calm. You have been creating storms in your life, never knowing you could also create the stars. Letting go of a struggle, which in reality doesn't exist, is allowing the stars to shine. Letting go of blocks and letting go of holding yourself back from doing what you are best driven to do is allowing the storm to rest. Confronting what you fear the most and allowing it to exist just as you do, is moving beyond the storm," Martin said, as the lights of the bus approached.

We hopped in. Home was closer this time.

"A spiritual walk is best walked every day of your life. You start your day at 'in' and you have grown when you are 'out' on the other side. You have evolved if you have calmed some storms and confronted some darkness and found purpose and success in what you do," Martin said, spreading his legs on the seat in front and letting out a big yawn.

I was tired too. I had a big awakened spirit excitedly alive in my small frame and I loved it.

We reached the cottage. I dropped the jacket and flung off my boots. "I will take these tomorrow," Martin said. "Sleep well." He kissed my forehead and disappeared into the starlit field.

When I slipped into bed that night I had understood the meaning of love. Love is growth, love is compassion, love is evolution, love is a lesson, love is allowing, love is granting life to be. I was in love, with all there was to be.

My experiences 'lessoned' for you:

•••> Love is what remains after beauty has passed.

•••> True love will last.

•••> Sometimes we inadvertently hurt others. In recognising this we find it easier to forgive others of the pain they brought us.

•••> You are exactly where your higher learning lies. And you are placed there to enable you to learn the lesson you need.

•••> Believe it or not you create your own storms and you create your own sunshine. That is the only truth there is.

•••> Sometimes you don't know what lies ahead and you will never know unless you move ahead.

•••> If you don't like the direction you are headed in, you can always make a turn.

•••> An apology is a declaration of your understanding and not an escape from facing up to your mistake.

•••> Being afraid does not make you small. You can't change something you can't first accept.

•••> Darkness is not the opposite of light. It is the absence of light. To beat the darkness you have to move towards the light of your own courage.

···> You don't need anyone's permission to be successful. If your work is serving your spiritual growth and also liberating others in the bargain, then you are a success.

···> There is no point in hanging on to the security and familiarity of the way in. In was the past. Out is the future. Your future.

···> Love is not the same as admiration. Love is growth, love is compassion, love is evolution, love is a lesson, love is in allowing and love is in granting life to be.

The Fire Walk Discovery

I had walked on fire four years before. In my youthful enthusiasm I had attended a seminar where I was made to walk on a ten feet long patch of burning embers. I was foolish enough to believe then that even fire could not burn me. I had got severely burnt and could not even walk back to my hotel room.

Before I had left for Bali to attend the fire walk, everyone had told me, "You are crazy! Fire burns! You will get hurt." And I had laughed. I was curious and wanted to find out for myself. But that night I kept my severe injury a secret, for it was easier to bear the pain of my burns than the sarcasm and ridicule of others. The burns healed but my curiosity was ignited. I wanted to know more. I wasn't done.

I spent four years tending fires. The moment I knew someone was conducting a fire walk I would willingly volunteer to tend the fire. Fire tending is the hardest part of a fire walk. Many spend decades tending fires before they can be initiated into leading fire walks. It is the fire tender who has the responsibility of building the fire, raking it out and making a fire bed for people to walk on. The greatest risk of injury lies with the fire tender because one can get dehydrated and collapse by mere exposure to the heat and flames while preparing the fire bed. I travelled across the globe tending fires for fire walk instructors. Sometimes I got burnt, sometimes others did. Every fire I tended was magical. It brought me closer to understanding the secrets of the human mind and the human spirit; secrets which can never be taught for they must be experienced.

But today I was nervous. I woke up in a cold sweat. I had been dreaming. I could not remember my dream as I opened my eyes but I could feel a sort of panic welling up.

"Since you have already fire walked and tended fires before, there is no point in you doing the fire walk again," Kahuna had told me at the salt cleanse. "This time you will lead it."

"Oh man, lead a fire walk!" I had thought in panic. I had never led a fire walk before. How can I when I have been burnt myself? How can I teach people that which I have not yet learnt fully? What was I to do? Every single day here at the farm was a challenge. There was no point in resistance really; every word uttered and every ritual initiated was an attempt towards spiritual liberation. I decided to go along with Kahuna's decision.

I was not ready to be a teacher. I never wanted to be a teacher yet that was what I had done all my life. I started teaching at the age of thirteen. I had just wanted to buy a new school uniform and so I taught my classmate for two months to collect enough money. I earned the money and bought the uniform but I had unwittingly taken on the responsibility of ensuring that my friend got good grades. I could not walk off mid way from the responsibility that came with earning the money. In the nine years that followed I taught 1900 students. I was the hippest hottest tuition teacher in my area and I was rich. That was the start of my working life and I never looked back. I started giving talks on various topics and found an appreciative audience. I soon became a professional speaker. I grew from there, conducting workshops for corporate houses, and before long I ended up being what I never really wanted to be: a teacher. And here I was again, all set to lead a group of people to walk on fire.

I was still sitting in bed, praying. "Oh Lord, please keep the people safe. No burning feet tonight. Not on my fire. Let not those who trust me get burnt". I put my trust in the Lord, assuming he had the time and inclination to listen to my prayers.

See, God meant convenience to me. I prayed when I needed him and made promises to him of what I would do if he gave me what I wanted. If there really was a God, which I didn't believe in my heart there was, I considered him incredibly stupid to play along with my crazy prayers and mad schemes.

I still remember I had walked twenty kilometers to a temple barefoot because it was said that by doing so you would be granted your wish. I walked twenty kilometers but nothing happened. With so many people flocking to the temple I guess I really had to fight for his attention and I failed. The next time I needed his help I had a better plan. The "prayer deal" I made was that if I passed my exam I would donate a thousand rupees to the poor. It worked. When I offered to help others in exchange for something I wanted I always got it. I'm a smart kid and God was like Big Daddy. If I pushed the right buttons I got what I wanted.

But today there was a lot at stake. It wasn't about what I wanted anymore; it was about others. Innocent people would walk on my fire, a fire that had burnt me severely in the past.

"Today is your big day," Emma remarked. She was genuinely very happy for me. Emma had been around for the rituals with Kahuna for many years now. Emma had never been allowed to lead a fire walk though she had assisted Kahuna on many. I wondered why I had been chosen and not she. I was surprised I asked myself that question because whenever it was a 'why me?' situation it was usually because I considered myself small. But today, I knew that someone else considered me bigger than I was and I so badly wanted to see myself through Kahuna's eyes.

"Yes," I grunted, "and I'm nervous."

"Your initiation starts in an hour," Emma smiled and left the room. She was always so bright, so tolerant and encouraging. I felt great in her presence.

Today I had the longest bath in many days. I was apprehensive about other people's trust and, most importantly, their belief that I could help them change their life; that if they could walk on fire, they could do anything.

I stepped down and saw that the breakfast area was converted into a prayer site. The huge rosewood table with the chairs was gone. The coffee pot and stove had been removed. There were mattresses on the floor with a square clearing in the centre. In it were placed a coral shell, sage leaves, balls of wool of different colours, an owl feather fan, some coloured square pieces of cloth tied with a string, my cat skin drum, and long sticks of wood.

The mattresses were arranged in a square set up. At the head of the square there was only one mattress, like the boss' seat in the boardroom. For the master, I thought.

I walked cautiously, trying not to step on the mattresses. Through the window I could see that breakfast had been served outside. Kahuna, Emma, Rick, Sain, and Mary were sitting at the garden table. I went out.

Rick stood up and offered me his seat. "Allow me to serve you," he winked and I could sense the respect in his voice. Everyone seemed genuinely happy for me. Even though Rick, Sain, and Emma had been with Kahuna for a long time and never led a fire walk, it did not lessen their excitement for mine.

"Have a hearty meal," Kahuna smiled. "Today is your day." Everyone clapped. Clapping is a ritual that awakens the energy within you and the environment. I clapped along, a little sheepishly though.

As we ate breakfast Sain shared some funny experiences about the sweat lodge and joked about some of the earlier participants. But my mind was only on the flames and the fire and the fire walk, and I prayed for mercy.

"Are you tired?" Kahuna asked, as breakfast came to an end.

I wasn't tired. I was unsure, in two minds. I was ready but I wasn't ready. It's a situation where your answer is yes and no at the same time. It's a situation where you want it and you don't want it, both together. While the war of uncertainty and doubt wages inside, we fake our peace to the world.

"No, I'm fine," I answered.

"Then let's go." Kahuna led us towards the prepared prayer site. We all took our seats on the mattress. I was made to sit opposite Kahuna, opposite the master. Emma lit the sage leaves and their soothing fragrance filled the room.

"You have been chosen to lead the fire tonight and many more fires to come. Today you will be initiated into a spiritual responsibility that you will fulfil by virtue of your deeds throughout your lifetime. The spiritual initiation does not end here. You are not just taking responsibility for the group of people who will walk your fire tonight but you are also taking responsibility for keeping the trust of all the people that you meet here on." With that Kahuna closed his eyes and began a chant. The others followed. I bowed my head, folded my hands, and surrendered my attention to the process.

The chant ended in a few minutes. Emma got up and handed us all bunches of coloured square cloth and wool. She gave me the ball of green wool. "Cut out pieces of the wool and knot them together," she instructed.

Obediently we all handed out the six balls of wool in turn to each other and snipped pieces of the yellow, green, white, red, blue, and black wool, knotting them all together to form a string.

"Place the six coloured cloths in different heaps," Emma continued. We did as directed, making six neat piles of cloth. There were four pieces of each colour.

Emma then brought forward a huge tray of what smelt like dried tobacco. I have a sharp nose and I could smell the tobacco despite the essence of the sage leaves. She placed the tray in the centre.

"Tobacco is a very potent herb," Kahuna explained. "It is used only for initiation into the spiritual world. The early shamans used tobacco in their rituals when they wanted to connect with the ether. It is said that when tobacco is prayed upon it will manifest your desires into reality; so be aware of what you wish for. You will take some tobacco in the palm of your hand, pray, plant your desire in it and neatly fold it in the coloured cloth given to you. Make it into a pouch, like a pouch of coins, and tie the mouth of it with the string of wool. Then take some more tobacco and pray and plant your desire in it, fold it in a piece of cloth and tie its mouth with the same string. So you will have a whole string of tobacco pouches strung together. This is called a prayer bead. The tobacco pouches will be like beads of a prayer necklace. There will be no conversation during the process. Emma and I will continue to chant and you will continue your process. Once the chant ends, your process ends with it, and that will complete your prayer beads." Kahuna did not wait for an acknowledgement nor did he ask if we had understood. He and Emma started to chant.

I was the first to reach out to the tray of tobacco and began to string in the tobacco beads. I prayed. I wanted to be a millionaire. With the next bead I wanted to be a billionaire. With the next one I wanted to be famous, I wanted to be world famous, I wanted to be admired, I wanted to be a multi billionaire, I wanted to be successful, I wanted to be a star, I wanted to be sexy, I wanted to be gorgeous, I wanted to be loved, I wanted to be a multi billionaire, I wanted to be a multi multi billionaire . . . and suddenly the chant came to a stop. I had the longest bead necklace in the whole group. Boy, I am fast; whether it is at prayer or knotting beads, I don't waste time. Everyone else had hardly five beads but my necklace went a long distance with thirteen. No one commented.

"We will offer the prayer beads for their manifestation in the ritual fire. This will be the fire of initiation, the fire of prayer. On its ashes will be built the fire for your walk tonight," Kahuna pointed in my direction.

"Before we go out Emma will cleanse your aura with the sage leaves. Hold on to your intention of service which will allow the manifestation of your desires." Kahuna got up and hastily walked out.

We all stood up and Emma took the sage leaves and whisked its smoky essence towards the body of every person from head to toe. I felt like a warrior being prepared for battle, only this time the battle was to defeat my little self and discover the gigantic indestructible spirit that I was.

We all walked out in a silent queue towards where the sweat lodge had been.

I remembered the pond, the desire ritual, the ritual of the talking stick and suddenly I found my level of belief and faith in myself rising. We all gathered at the spot where the fire pit to heat the lava rocks was made.

"We will bring the wood from the barn," Kahuna said. He tied in the spot of the fire pit with the red wool, making an outline around it.

"Only you come with me," Kahuna said, pointing in my direction. He walked ahead and I had to walk two steps at a time to keep pace with him.

We reached the barn where we had done the salt cleanse and I almost smiled to myself. That was one hell of a test to survive. The chickens were back, I could hear them clucking inside. Kahuna opened the door of the cubicle which a few days ago had been a makeshift toilet. It was now stocked with piles of dry wood.

"This is the pine wood which we will use to build the fire for the fire walk tonight," he pointed to the left. "And on the right is teak wood which we will use for the initiation ritual. Teak wood is never used for a fire walk."

Looking at my frown he laughed out loud and said, "Teak burns at about 4000°F – 5000°F and produces very sharp coal. Only a master moves through heat that strong. Pine burns at 2000°F – 2500°F and produces softer coal. Teak is a severe fire; however a fire that severe serves only the initiation ritual.

Kahuna picked up a log of wood and touched it to his head. He looked at me and motioned me with his eyes to do the same. I picked up the heavy teak log and touched it to my head. We walked back to the fire pit. The log was extremely heavy and I was happy to reach the pit. Rick had already put in some dried leaves, twigs and sticks. Had placed his log of wood in the pit and I placed mine over his making a cross.

Rick bent over and lit the fire. Kahuna and the others broke out into a chant, looking skywards. I looked up too. The sun was still on the rise, warm and friendly. The sky was a clear blue. No clouds. Apart from the occasional flight of an eagle, the sky was still. A straight line of smoke began to build up and rise towards the sky. It was the kind of smoke that stranded travellers build on an island to get the attention of passing ships. This girl is lost; you need to get her back to the shores of sanity, seemed the plea!

"The initiation ritual is about making a connection between earth and ether. Your desires are transported through the burning tobacco, through the smoke, through the flames, to the ethereal world. The ethereal world is where all is granted. It's the plane of effortless operation and effortless manifestation. Ether knows no struggle. 'Your wish is my command' is the order of ether," Kahuna explained, as I watched the trail of smoke disappearing into the sky in a magically straight line.

"The element of fire is the only element that stands for transformation. Whatever is offered in the fire is transformed. It is not changed because change is reversible—it is transformed. When matter transforms it loses its molecular and chemical composition and forms matter different from that which existed. When you offer wood in the fire, it exists in some chemical and molecular composition with can be decoded by scientists to define it as 'wood'. When this is touched by fire, it turns into coal, a mass of carbon leaving its earlier form behind. This carbon allows the wood the potential of a diamond through its transformation. From tree to diamond is a spiritual transformation."

It took me a while to digest that and Kahuna continued without pausing, "The ritual states that when a live human body steps upon live fire or cinders, it is transformed in proportion to the prayer offered upon building it. So when you pray upon the fire and walk on it, you become the

prayer. The prayer is no longer outside you, you become it."
I was mesmerised.

This was THE answer to all my questions. I sought effortless
living and effortless loving, and here was my answer.

Kahuna bent down and took a handful of mud. He brought it
up and released it slowly. He was checking the direction of
the wind. The wind was blowing south-west, he said.

Rick and Emma opened up what are called "prayer flags".
Prayer flags are small square pieces of cloth of six different
colours tied together with a white string. They are like those
stringed decorations you have in birthday parties only that
on the prayer flags ancient hymns and prayers are written.

Rick and Emma stood across the fire holding the prayer flags
end to end as they fluttered wildly in the breeze.

"The prayer flags will protect your desires from harming
others. Sometimes in the pursuit of one's desires and
happiness one unknowingly hurts or harms others and that
pain restricts him from fully enjoying the fruits of his hard
work. A dedicated employee works long hours to get a raise
to put his children in better schools but misses out on being
with them because he has no time. The children go to a
better school but miss out on the affection of their father
and no one is happy. The prayer flags protect the well-being
of the person who has expressed his prayer and desire and
also protect the well-being of all others concerned. So when
your desires manifest, they do so in a manner that protects
the well being of all those who are connected with you."

Kahuna began to chant and the flames of the fire grew
higher. The smoke disappeared. Hot, violent flames leapt
into the air, the kind of flames that burn and sting your
flesh. I was tempted to move back but I held my ground.

"We will now string the fire with the prayer beads. Try to tie the flames with the string and adorn the flames with the prayer necklace you have just made. While doing that, each one of you will speak your prayer aloud.

Emma went first, garlanding the flames with her prayer bead necklace. "This is for world peace," she said.

Rick went next and in one stroke his garland was consumed by the flames, "This is for Mother Earth," he said.

Sain offered his prayer beads, saying, "This is for peace and spiritual freedom."

I was next and I was wildly embarrassed. How was I to top world peace, well being for Mother Earth, and spiritual liberation? How was I to confess to my prayer to be a multi-billionaire?

I offered my really long necklace to the flames. "I want to be a multi-billionaire," I said, embarrassed. And I could hear a crow cawing his disapproval from a nearby tree.

If Kahuna had only told us earlier that we would have to say our prayers out aloud, I would have certainly asked for world peace.

The flames began to dance and fresh new white smoke welled up as I saw my prayer beads gulped by the flames till they turned to ash.

We sat watching the flames dance and die out only to dance again with every draught. Rick and Emma stood guard, protecting our prayers with the prayer flags.

The sun came up strong. I don't know what was hotter, the sun or the heat from the fire. We sat around until the last ember turned to ash.

Kahuna scooped up a handful of warm ash and smudged some in my hair. "Leave it on," he instructed. "This will remind you that in all you do and all you achieve, what you have is this, ash. You will build that which the fire cannot touch and the flames cannot destroy. That will be your salvation."

He continued, "To be a multi-billionaire is a great prayer and it is a prayer that invites greater responsibility because you only become a billionaire when people accept and acknowledge your service to be genuine and priceless. You don't become a billionaire because you want to. You become a billionaire because you add value, because you change people, because you improve the world with your contribution." Kahuna gently touched my forehead again and walked towards the cottage as I stood there, humbled.

It was celebration time and Mary had prepared a feast. We ate to our heart's content. "You can sleep on the mattress down here. This is your abode for the day. The fire walk ritual will start in the evening at 6.00 p.m. We have invited people to come by 5.30 so you have time to interact with them. Jacques and René will be your fire tenders and you will instruct them on building your fire. We will all be your students in your session and you will be our master. I release my position to you. May the force be with you!" Kahuna placed his hand on my head and locked me in a long and tight embrace.

I went over the instructions and rehearsed the process in my head. I lay down on the mattress and closed my eyes. I knew I would not sleep but I needed to rest my eyes, still smarting from all the smoke.

Just a few minutes on the mattress and I got up. This was a big responsibility. I sure needed the energy but my spirit was too alive. I walked out and spotted Emma. "Where can I find Jacques and René?" I asked. I needed to explain to them how I wanted my fire built. This would be their first time at tending the fire, just as it would be my first time leading it.

"Oh, there they are," she said, pointing to the two figures under a tree nearby.

Jacques and René were sitting under the tree, smoking a cigarette. I walked towards them and apologised for the interruption. "Can we do a dry run for the fire walk? Like a rehearsal. So I can explain to you exactly how I want the fire to be built?" I asked.

Jacques and René jumped to their feet. Jacques spat out his cigarette but René continued to smoke. I walked them towards the barn and showed them the wood pile.

"We will build five layers of the pine wood," I explained. It was beautiful, dry pine wood. It would make a very magnificent fire; I could already visualise the flames and the cinders.

We then walked to the fire pit where the ritual had just been held. The embers were still alive, and when a breeze blew gently, mysterious smoke emerged in that same magical straight line.

"Our prayers are still alive," I smiled. I could literally see the counters in my bank account rolling with the additional zeros.

"You will build five layers of the pine wood on the fire pit, right here at the centre. You start the fire with the prayer. Offer sage at intervals. The fire must never be left unattended. It's like leaving a prayer ritual unguarded. One of you will always be by the fire side. I will be inside conducting the session and you will be holding the fire for me outside. I will be out in forty-five minutes from the start of my session. Once I am out, you will help me rake the fire bed. Is that clear or do you want to ask me something?" I asked like a master on a mission.

Jacques and René nodded that they understood. It's scary

when people don't ask questions. You don't know whether they have understood correctly. I decided to trust in the process.

"And no smoking by the fire side," I turned and smiled as I headed back to the cottage. That was my rule. I was the master for the day.

I sat on the mattress preparing my talk. I would start with the history of fire walking and then move the topic to how ordinary people can fire walk without getting burnt. It was mind over matter. Rather, it was mind in matter. The human body is an amazing device. It changes chemically and hormonally with the situation. If allowed the time to mentally prepare to walk on fire, the body will secrete sweat, raise the heart beat, pump in adrenaline and a dozen other hormones and chemicals which will take the body through 2500 degrees of heat and burning coal unscathed. That is the purpose of the fire walk, to demonstrate that when you make up your mind and take action, your body follows. The past is not equal to the future; just because you got burnt in the past does not mean that you will get burnt today. The fire walk demonstrates that past burns are accidents; they were not intentional. But if you are aware of the burning coals and if you purposefully walk on them, then you are acting in awareness and in full intention. And there is no fire that can touch a spirit that is ignited to it's true power. As children we have played with fire and flames and never got burnt. It was only when we were not paying attention that we got injured. Life can be an accident where you live every day in ignorance and wonder why everything burns, or you can live life with purpose and awareness and create the magic of walking through adversities unharmed. It is when you match the spirit of the fire that your spirit is set free.

I was excited with my preparation and I could not wait for my session to begin. This would be the biggest day of my life.

I saw people arriving exactly on time. Four families walked in—parents with their children. This was not the crowd that I had expected. They were villagers from nearby, friends of Kahuna's. I smiled at them but did not approach them. I was trying to keep my attention on my speech; I did not want to engage in small talk. That's what I used to do before every seminar back home.

At five minutes to six I got up. I thought I would start with a polite welcome and thank the people for coming. I had half a mind to tell a very distracted lady to sit out with her wailing child. Something had put the little girl off and she was bawling non-stop. This would be an interesting seminar, I told myself.

I approached the lady closest to me. She wore a long skirt and a short coat. She looked about thirty. She held her one-year-old baby boy in her arms. I smiled and touched the boy's head, "What's his name?" I started my small talk. The lady simply smiled back.

"What's his name?" I asked again, assuming she had not heard me. The lady turned around to her husband and said something in Dutch. The husband came towards us, smiling.

"Hello, my name is Priya," I stretched out my hand. "Dmitris," he said, shaking my hand.

I was confused. Emma came to my rescue. "Oh, this is Annie and Dmitris. They don't speak English."

"What!" I exclaimed in my head. I turned around to the others who were now getting seated on the mattress. "They don't either," Emma said as she scurried to help the lady with her bawling daughter.

"Huh?" I was supposed to lead a fire walk with a bunch of

villagers who did not speak English. "What is going on? Why? Why? Kahuna knew it. Why didn't he say anything? Was he crazy!!!!! These people would burn. What would I tell them? How would they know? This was absolutely insane.

Tears began to well up in my eyes and I turned around pretending to get a glass of water. I felt cheated. All my preparation went to waste. "How will I talk to people who don't understand my language? How will I get them to walk on fire? God, help! I will give food to the girl's orphanage for one week, one full week. Get me through this. Save my soul," I prayed to my God of convenience.

Kahuna sounded the gong, bringing things to order. He stood up and addressed the crowd in Dutch and introduced me. I assumed he introduced me because I heard my name and every few seconds the crowd turned and smiled in my direction. I have no idea what Kahuna told them and I hoped he told them I didn't speak Dutch.

With another gong, Kahuna said, "All yours!"

"I will pray every single day. I will acknowledge you every single day! Save me this one time," I prayed to God, a promise I knew I would never keep.

I took a deep breath and started my talk. "Hello, my name is Priya and I am from India." And halfway through my sentence I realised the absurdity of what I was doing. Everyone was looking at me with attention. The little girl had stopped crying and I didn't know what I was saying anymore.

"I'm afraid," I said. "I'm afraid that you don't understand what I have to say. And I am sorry I don't know how to explain to you what is going to happen and why it is going to happen. But when we do go out, there will be a fire burning." And suddenly I got up and started to wave my hands and put life in all that I was saying. It was as though I was playing the game of dumb charades, explaining to people how and why they would walk on fire and how their life would change after that.

My audience was attentive, picking up every gesture, every sound, and every intention. Every so often they would break into a conversation with each other and there would be nods from others and then they would turn to me for approval. I would nod, hoping that whatever the discussion was, it was in the right direction.

I spoke a weird language. No one objected. They knew they were there for a fire walk. No one objected. They knew they had no clue about how to do it. They knew they had no clue about why it was possible. They knew they were unaware of what they would gain out of the fire walk. All they knew was that if Kahuna was there and I was there and they were invited, it was good for them.

Where has that kind of faith gone? Where are those people whose invitation and presence is greater than any sermon or talk? Where are those people who have the capacity to believe in the system enough to walk on any fire in faith?

How much money is spent on hard talk to sell things we don't really need! Billions of dollars are spent in making people believe in having things they never knew existed and in building experiences they didn't want. So much time is wasted in making people believe that if they don't own something, they are inferior in some way. What a cruel way of communication and what a callous waste of money.

I guess what flows more clearly than words is your intention and your spirit. You really don't need words to convince; your intention and your presence is enough. Words are cheap but what people really buy is your intention, which reveals itself whether you know it or not. There is a listening beyond words and that is the call of the spirit.

As I led the people out to the fire that night, their bodies were already preparing for the walk. You don't have to tell your heart to beat; it knows its job. You don't tell your body to release the adrenaline at the sight of the flames; it does so without your knowing. You don't explain to your body to produce the necessary chemicals in an instant combined with a release of sweat to protect your feet; it does so in an attempt to sustain life. Your body is doing all that it can endlessly, tirelessly, while you sleep, while you play, while you work. It works intently day in and day out to keep you alive, without your instruction and without your knowledge. Your body does not need your permission to survive; it does so because it was designed for it.

And even if there was something you could say to your body right here, right now, in front of the flames, what would you say? What would you tell it to do? What do you know about yourself? What do you know about your ability? This isn't about you doing the fire walk. This is about you discovering who you are and what you are capable of.

Everything cannot be explained. And yet everything happens.

How can you walk on fire without burning? There are several contradictory theories. What is real is that fire does not burn a mind that is made up. The body becomes bigger than the fire and moves through it. The body becomes the fire and embraces it.

As we walked out there was non-stop chatter. I had no idea what was being discussed but the energy was unstoppable.

We walked towards the fire, now burnt down to embers. My talk had obviously taken longer than I expected or the fire had burned down faster than it should have.

I started to rake out the coals, building a neat runway.

The fire bed was not very long. I didn't build it that long. I strongly believe that it's not about how many steps you take on the fire; it's all about the first step. If the first step gets you through, then the next step will.

I built a beautiful fire bed peppered with gleaming embers. It looked magical.

I looked at the group that stood in silence observing me with fire in their eyes and faith in their hearts. These people needed no pep talk. They were naturals. Anyone who sits through a fire walk talk without understanding the language is ready for life. I was simply playing "master" for myself. These people needed no lesson, they were teaching me with their presence.

I guess everyone we meet in life is a potential master; they all bring our lessons with them. Only some foolish ones like me need to travel to the other part of the world to seek one.

"Fire walking is not a joke," I broke the chatter with a command in my voice, knowing very well they would not understand a word. But I had moved beyond words now. "Fire walking is a spiritual pathway. It is a door towards a reality which is giving you a chance to create it. Fire transforms. Fire moves. Fire ignites. And when you walk this fire tonight, may you never be the same again!"

I beckoned to my fire tenders to take position. They were sweating profusely despite the extreme cold.

"This is a hot fire," I said to myself as I patted the last coals to make a clean, neat fire bed.

"The fire bed is open," I said as I looked up to heaven in prayer. The sky was lit with the same star-like embers as the fire bed. I stepped away. The group walked and danced on the fire one after the other, squealing and laughing. This was amazing. They were hugging each other in delight and talking frantically. I loved this. I don't know what they understood but once they were at the fire, their minds took over and their bodies instinctively knew what to do.

"Let's get some flames up," Kahuna said. It's nice to have flames on the sides of the runway; it adds magic to the walk.

"We will have to get some more wood," Jacques said, looking at me.

"You stay by the fire; I will run and get some logs." I broke into a run towards the barn, René following suit. I was almost panting as I flung open the cubicle door. I turned left to pick up some wood, hoping that some was left over.

"Thank god there is a huge pile," I said as I plucked out three logs and handed them to René, and began to pile three logs in my arms. As I shut the cubicle door with my foot, a chill of horror ran up my spine. The logs tumbled out of my arms. I flung the door open again. The entire pile of pine wood was intact, untouched. The pile of teak wood was gone.

I felt dizzy and wanted to vomit. "Are you ok?" I heard René asking in panic.

"Where is this pile of wood?" I asked René, pointing to the empty space and praying he would not say what I knew he would. "We built the fire with it," he said with sincerity.

That was teak wood burning at the fire pit. That was teak wood on which the poor innocent villagers were walking. "Teak wood is never used in fire walking. It makes the hottest fire and produces the sharpest coals." I remembered Kahuna's words. I felt weak and could not muster up the courage to go back.

"Are you ok?" René asked again.

I regained my composure. I had no option; the teak wood was already burning. I took a deep breath. I was the master after all, for today at least. I walked back in prayer with three logs of wood in my arms.

The group of villagers had stopped walking. I was half expecting them to be crying in pain and cursing me. But when they saw me another wave of excitement built up. I put down the logs of wood on the sides and Jacques lit them up in glorious flames. Then Kahuna led the group into a fire dance ritual.

I stood on the side, motionless. What had I done? My first fire walk, my first initiation on teak wood. And these people were rejoicing!

The thing was, I knew that was teak wood, they didn't. I think if I had poured hot lava instead of coals they would have walked on that unharmed too. They had believed in Kahuna, in me, and most importantly, in themselves. That made them evolved beings.

The last of the embers were stomped upon and a sweaty lot of people were set free.

"The fire bed will now be closed," I took over again. "May your belief and your prayers be safe and· find the most magical and joyous manifestation in your life." I had no more words to say, I was choked with emotion.

Emma led the group back inside for coffee and cake.

I sat down next to the embers that had been so well walked upon. Jacques smiled, "That was a beautiful fire. I have never seen a fire like this before. It was magical." I just smiled back without saying a word; I didn't want to take away his happiness by accusing him of being careless with the wood. It had been a magical process after all. A fire walk with teak wood, a seminar in a foreign language, and no burns at all!

Faith and belief are magical things. They transform the ordinary into the extraordinary. They are the two potent emotions that lead us to our breakthroughs. Because where is the limit really? And who sets it? It is your own limitation and your own belief that will eventually hold true for you.

Most of us have limiting beliefs and we tell ourselves unworthy things. A great author once said, "God will forgive you for your sins, your nervous system won't." It is important to remember that your mind is only a slave to your beliefs.

Kahuna sat down beside me. "That was miraculous. You are an amazing master. Truly wonderful, a sheer joy. The people are raving about you and your energy."

"You knew they didn't speak English, right?" I asked Kahuna in an almost accusing tone.

"Is that the language for teaching?" Kahuna quizzed me. "You can learn from the birds, the frogs, the trees, the sun, and the seasons. Which language must they speak so that you can learn? Is there a language for love? Does one really have to tell you that he hates you for you to know that? There is no language for teaching and there is no language for learning. You can learn life's greatest lessons without anyone having said a word. And you can teach lessons of a million lifetimes with your sheer presence. That is the gift of a great master."

I had tears in my eyes. "I failed," I confessed. "The boys burnt the teak wood instead of pine. The people walked on teak wood." And I began to sob like a child.

"Look at me," Kahuna said, taking my face in his hands.

"People will mess up in your path. People will be negligent in the way of your purpose. There will be mistakes on the part of others, sometimes innocent, sometimes intentional. But what remains in the end and drives the result is who you are. People did not walk on the fire bed made by Jacques or René. They walked on your energy and your force. And your energy is greater than any teak wood put together; such is the force of the master. It is the master alone, the soul that is ignited to its purpose that can turn poison into the cup of life. It is the power of the master to negate any hurdle in the path of the follower's belief. It is the power of the master to be an answer to the prayers of others in every circumstance. It is the master alone who can have a fire bed of teak and yet ensure that his people remain unharmed. You are the master. You are the one."

"It is your force that will take millions along any fire because you are there, holding a spiritual responsibility. And when you assume that role, know that you are not alone. You are backed by a thousand others whose spirit you represent and whose spirit you have ignited."

Kahuna left me alone by the fire, by my fire, and walked to the cottage to say goodbye to his guests.

I was mesmerised, facing my own power, seeing myself through Kahuna's eyes.

I waited by the fire until what seemed like eternity. Jacques' voice intruded upon my thoughts, startling me. "Kahuna is calling you," he said.

I got up slowly and walked with Jacques towards the cottage.

The villagers had gone. Kahuna and the others were already seated in the same place as the morning. There was a small statue of the Buddha in the centre where all the tobacco and woollen balls had lain.

As I took my position, Kahuna spoke, "We have come to the end of the initiation process and we now declare you a spiritual master, a spiritual healer. Your presence and your purpose will heal. You have been initiated into the fire." He lit up the sage leaves.

"The fire has accepted you. Know that there are several fires that people represent. There is a fire that destroys the forest, and then there is fire that heals; there is a fire that burns in glory and then there is fire that cooks and transforms. There is a fire that warms and gives life and there is the one that you represent—it is the bonfire, the fire of celebration! You are a celebration, you are a joy. Your presence brings joy and laughter and life. May you be the fire of celebration and may people celebrate life in your company!"

"The initiation is over," Kahuna concluded.

He got up and bent over the statue of the Buddha. He took off an orange crystal necklace from the statue and knelt down in front of me.

"In you I see the goddess of fire. In you I see the goddess of power. In you I see the goddess of love. May your life be a discovery of your own divinity and may your work be that of worship in service of others." With those words he slipped the necklace around my neck and in an instant, without permission, everyone came forward and took me in an embrace. I was hugged by nine people at the same time and I knew I had been accepted. I had been initiated.

That night was a night of completion. I knew the real fire walk would start from there. My real spiritual challenge was to create and shape the days to come with the knowledge of the growth and freedom I had experienced there.

Rick and Sain were walking outside and Emma was in conversation with Mary at the garden table. I was exhausted. I went up and crashed on my bed. I was sweaty and smelt of smoke, but it didn't matter. I checked my ticket which lay neatly by my bedside. At this time tomorrow I would be home, I thought.

A whole week had gone by in the blink of an eye. I had only just arrived.

When I came to Netherlands seven days ago, I did so to escape from a world that had meticulously collapsed. I was hurting when I took that flight. I was heartbroken and shattered. And here I was now, healed faster than I had been hurt.

But when I look back at what I had done in coming here to attend the rituals, I don't think I had been escaping. Escape is when you move into denial that something is wrong and that something needs to be done about it. I was aware that my life was messed up and I was aware I needed to change it drastically. How can that be an escape from reality? I had done the right thing by coming here, by allowing myself to learn new ways, the right ways of living. Until then I had been living by the same old rules of compromise, blame, and regret. I had done the right thing by saying no to all that did not feel right and flying out in search of a better answer, a better way of life. And I had found it. I had lived and experienced the answer. I had done the right thing; I smiled to myself with a sense of pride.

The rituals had done me good. I did not have a single minute to grieve over my past. Participating in the rituals took my pain away and opened me up to a new world of good and powerful possibilities. I was empowered, I was awakened. I was no longer the victim of the world; I was now the creator.

I felt grateful for all my experiences and my heart humbled with love at the support I had received. Each and every person that I met was a master in his or her own right: Emma, Rick, Sain, Mary, everyone. In allowing me my growth and spiritual evolution they had taught me lessons of support, tolerance, and unconditional love.

Way back home, everyone's life seemed a mess. No one really seemed happy. They wanted to be happy but it always remained a want, it never became their reality. Happiness is not something that you want, happiness is not a desire. Happiness is something you give, happiness is in the act of doing. For them happiness was always something that "happened" to you. It never occurred to them that you create your own happiness. Happiness is a choice, not a consequence. Happiness is not something others give you; happiness is something you give others, because you have it. Happiness is not something you can keep for yourself. Happiness, literally, is an emotion of selfless sharing; whether you like it or not, when you are happy you spread it. You cannot contain happiness just like you cannot contain the fragrance of a rose. Happiness does not belong to you, happiness belongs to the world because when you are happy the world lights up in joy.

And because they didn't know any better, their advice and concern was only coloured by their own experience of compromise. "You can't have your cake and eat it too. You can't have everything. You will have to compromise at every stage. You can't trust people. It's a bad world out there . . ." Their reality was defined by such beliefs, which they perpetuated without questioning.

I did not want that kind of life. I was done with my share of compromise. My spirit is too big to compromise. I feel there is enough for everyone, and compromise is a word for those who don't want to grow and share. For a spirit that is driven by growth and evolution there is co-existence, never compromise. Compromise is the fastest way to kill your spirit. And I had always wanted to be free.

Here I was, as free as free could be. I knew that I would continue to be guided and loved and blessed; that my journey had just begun. I knew that to keep this energy alive I had to become Kahuna, Mary, Emma, Rick, Sain, Ruud, Martin, Jacques, and René for others. I knew that in keeping their essence of love and support alive in my daily intention I would be able to guide myself to my purpose every day.

My journey had now truly begun. If my spiritual growth was for real then I would be able to create a better world for myself no matter where I went. If my realisations and experiences had truly touched my heart and stirred up power and compassion in me, then I could evolve in any circumstance. I knew what I had gained was real, and I was ready to re-create my world over the ashes of the old one.

I prayed and I surrendered. In seven magical days I had recognised my power and I had faced my fears. I was liberated. My whole life lay ahead of me, a life I had carefully designed in prayer for the past seven days.

My experiences 'lessoned' for you:

...> You don't always need to know before you teach. Sometimes in your teaching is your greatest learning.

...> It takes a high degree of greatness to rejoice in the achievement and victory of others. Only the small live in envy.

...> When you desire to be rich you invite responsibility to add value to people's lives. You become a billionaire when people accept and acknowledge your service to be genuine and priceless.

...> Some lessons cannot be explained, some lessons just have to be experienced by walking the fire.

...> Everyone we meet in life is a potential master; they all bring your lessons with them.

...> When fear knocks on the door and faith opens it, nobody is there!

...> You can learn life's greatest lessons without anyone having said a word. And you can teach lessons of a million lifetimes with your sheer presence.

...> It is ignorance that burns; fire is just an excuse.

...> When the mind is made up, the body unites with the force of the circumstance to create the desired reality, whether it is to walk the fire or build an empire.

...> Your life is best lived when life becomes a celebration for those whom you touch.

...> You are the master and you are the student. Life will teach you both ways.

...> Happiness is a choice and when you make that choice to be happy, you can't help but spread it.

The Beginning

- -

"I am the master," I smiled to myself.

I was the master of my own destiny. I was the master of my own life. I was the master of what I did and of what happened to me. I was the master of the past, using it to help my spiritual evolution, and I was the master of my future, which was my chance to put those lessons to use. I was free.

I had very cleverly trapped myself all these years. Most of us do. We are like a majestic peacock—bright feathers, proud gait, a bird of envy and admiration— who walks very intently into a cage. And then, when no one is looking, he cleverly locks the cage from the inside and throws the key far away. And for the rest of its life he wails and lives in self pity and defeat until one day someone recognises his spirit and gives him back the key, saying, "Hey, what are you doing in this cage? You were meant to be free."

We find our freedom and we think it is the master who freed us. The master merely handed us the key to the lock we had turned in the first place. It is in our crying out for help that we attract the attention of the master, who hands us the key which we had unwittingly thrown away.

I was a very strong peacock because I had thrown the key so far that I had to fly halfway across the planet to retrieve it.

"Hurry up," Emma came running. "Your taxi is already here."

I didn't want to leave this perfect world. It was that altruist world I had always imagined in my head. But if a beautiful world existed there, then I could potentially create it back home too. The responsibility of creating it was mine. "If not me, then who?" I smiled.

I took my rucksack; there was not much to carry back. I took off the fur coat and gave it to Mary. "This is yours now!" she said. I didn't know when I would next need an oversized fur coat but I had learnt not to refuse a well intended gift. I slipped it right on, giving her a hug.

Rick and Sain gave me a group hug. Rick ruffled my hair; he knew it irritated me and loved to see the expression on my face. "Next time," Sain pointed a finger towards my nose, "no clothes on while sleeping." And we all laughed.

Martin was waiting at the door. I looked at him with the eyes of a lover who will never see her beloved again. Martin took my hand and pressed something in it. I opened my palm and saw a small marble egg. "This is the egg of possibilities. It could hatch into any possibility. Which possibility? You decide!" I held on to the egg tightly and Martin gave me a hug. "Shine bright," he said. "I will see your light wherever I am!"

Kahuna was standing near the taxi. He opened his arms. "The goddess of celebration," he said, giving me a big hug.

"Create your magic. Spread your love and spread your light. Create a celebration wherever you go. Make this a world of celebration and joy so that the gods look down and say, 'Hey there's a party happening there, let's go too'. Let your life and your work be an invitation to the gods to come and celebrate their creation," he said, putting me into the taxi.

"I am another you," Kahuna whispered as the taxi took off.

As we drove past the fields I knew that I had found myself. "Remember to take your baggage," the driver smiled, looking in the rear view mirror.

"I'm not carrying any baggage back," I laughed. "Give my stuff away to anyone who needs it."

"It will be difficult to find someone your size," he chuckled and we laughed our way to the station.

It was the beginning of the rest of my life.

My experiences 'lessoned' for you:

···> There is only one destiny, the one you design for yourself.

···> The master is already within. How you can expect someone else to sort out the world you messed up?

···> Sometimes the hardest task is to "un-create" the mess which we have got ourselves in.

···> The test of learning is how you apply it to make your life and the lives of others better.

···> There exists a perfect world if you care enough to create it.

···> Today is the beginning of the rest of your life. You can start at any point you want.

···> We are all granted the gift of choosing possibilities. When you choose a certain possibility you start the process of its manifestation. Despair is as much your choice as abundance is.

···> I am another you . . . If I can, you already have.

Afterword

∙ ∙

I returned from the Netherlands in May 2004 and my life has never been the same ever since. It is as though I am living a brand new life.

Until then I had read many books and many teachers had shaped my perception of the world. The rituals that I took part in were lessons of many lifetimes that I learnt in three weeks. I participated in thirteen rituals but have written about the five most valuable ones in this book. In my experience with the shamans I not only gained knowledge but also the power of applied wisdom and compassion. I am now able to adapt and adjust to any situation and I am able to see a higher meaning for my existence. That discovery in itself makes every day a step towards my growth and further evolution.

Friends and others who read the manuscript in the preparatory stages have told me that while reading it they felt as though they had themselves been through the processes I went through. They felt the breakthrough I made, they could identify with my struggle and they rejoiced in my victory. And that was my greatest joy because that was my intention in writing the book.

We will never live long enough to make all the mistakes we can and we will never live long enough to make up for the mistakes we realised we did. In sharing my experience I hope to prevent you from repeating mine and to help you to realise your own potential.

Today I feel that the greatest lessons are the ones that are learnt daily. You really don't need to visit the shamans or take an escapist trip. The lessons can be found right where you are if you just care to look. This book was one of your "daily" doses. If you just look around, your lesson, your ticket to a better you, is waiting just around the corner. All you need is the desire to move forward into the unknown with the belief that you will be led to a better life.

On a parting note I would like to say that in writing about my journey I have tried to reach out to you, to connect with you, because in touching your life I have grown in mine, because in spending time with you through this book I have enriched my purpose, because in having you connect with me I have healed my life. If I have touched even one life and transformed it for the better my turmoil has been worth it.

Your Journey Begins Here

Even though I came back home from the Netherlands in 2004, my journey, my search for a better self, continued. I carry on looking for goodness and I let my curiousity guide me towards excellence. I have ever since maintained my student status by learning from life and people every day. Every ritual I had undergone had a practical lesson and that learning has been so ingrained in me that I live by every learning that touched my heart.

This book has given me the opportunity to connect with like minded people. If you have reached so far, then you and I certainly have something in common, a quest for spiritual freedom through a life well-lived.

I would like our journey to continue, I would like this connection to grow, and I encourage you to share and exchange your thoughts on how you have grown into the wonderful person you are. I am inviting you to join me, and many others like us, so that we can always count upon each other to be held and helped through our own journeys in life.

My team and I have identified some platforms where we can communicate and share our life towards a better world. There is more to the book . . . this is not the end. We are opening the book to an experience. We will be organising events in cities across India and many other countries where we will be holding forums for self improvement and we will also be conducting certain rituals to allow you your own learning. You can stay connected and recieve invitations to all our events and work. Please remember, you have heard my story and I am humbled with your attention and time. I now look forward to being enriched by yours.

Waiting to connect with you.

Priya Kumar

You can connect with Priya Kumar on the following platforms.

1. Facebook: username: Priya Kumar
2. Twitter: http://twitter.com/kumarpriya
3. Blogger: http://iamanotheryouthebook.blogspot.com
4. Website: www.priya-kumar.com

1. DS
2. Algo
3. Windows via C/C++
4. WI
5. C
6. C++
7. DP